D1029308

TIMBER
ITS DEVELOPMENT AND DISTRIBUTION

One of the Byzantine Mosaics on the Walls of the Cathedral, Monreale, Sicily, showing Carpenters and Joiners at Work on the Ark

TIMBER

Its Development
and Distribution

A Historical Survey

BY

BRYAN LATHAM

GEORGE G. HARRAP & CO. LTD

LONDON TORONTO WELLINGTON SYDNEY

First published in Great Britain 1957
by GEORGE G. HARRAP & CO. LTD
182 High Holborn, London, W.C.1

*Composed in Bembo type and printed by
Morrison & Gibb Ltd, London and Edinburgh*

Made in Great Britain

To
ANNE

PREFACE

IT has seemed to me for some time past that the story of timber and the timber trade, which, legend apart, has a historical record of at least three thousand years, well merited putting into a book. I have been further spurred to action by the kindly pressure of many friends, who have done me the honour of reading my articles and listening to my lectures on the manifold and fascinating aspects of timber. They have continually told me that these matters should be safely enshrined in a book, so here is the book !

The collection of the material, the facts, the names, and the dates which go to fill these pages has most pleasurably occupied me for the past ten years. I feel that I have been among the most fortunate of authors in being able to combine an enthralling interest with my daily round. Many people have asked me how I was able to find the time to do the necessary research and to collate the information. The answer is, whether I am working or playing, that timber is in my blood, as it has been in the blood of my ancestors for two hundred years past.

I am grateful to timber for the delightful people I was able to meet in all walks of life while gathering the material for this book. Such friends include timber-men at home and abroad, foresters, research workers, scientists, technologists, and the hosts of wood-users. Firstly, I am especially indebted to the proprietors of *Wood* for permission to use material from my articles already published in their admirable magazine, and also for the use of illustrations. As indicated, I owe my facts and background sketches to a great number of persons and sources. With regard to the great timber territories of the U.S.A., I must take this opportunity of especially acknowledging my debt to Mr Elwood R. Maunder and Miss Lillian M. Willson, of the Forest Products History Foundation, Inc., Minnesota, also to Mr Stanley F. Horn both for his books and the early columns of his seventy-five-years-old *Southern Lumberman*, which celebrated its Diamond Jubilee in 1956. Mr David Gillies and Miss Charlotte Whitton have rendered me an equal service for Canada and the Ottawa Valley in their carefully documented record *A Hundred Years A-Fellin'*, *1842-1942*. Farther west I have delved into the historical notes of the British Columbia Lumber and Shingle Manufacturers' Association. Nearer home I found *Swedish Timber Exports*, *1850-1950*, by the Swedish Wood Exporters' Association, a veritable mine of information for Swedish statistics.

In connexion with historical research, I am greatly indebted to the Librarian and staff of the Timber Development Association for checking figures and facts for me over a decade. Also to the Librarian, Mr J. F. Mason, and staff of the Hyde Institute and Barnet Public Library, for their wonderful perseverance in hunting the country for books long out of print, and their loaning their finds to me for unlimited periods.

Finally, I am grateful to Miss Grace Tanner for helping me to collect, collate, and file historical timber references over a number of years, also for assisting me to compile that bane of all authors, the index !

B. L.

CONTENTS

ILLUSTRATIONS

CHAPTER I

AN ANCIENT TRADE

TIMBER was the first building material used by man to provide himself with shelter when he emerged from the primeval cave. Its story is one of enthralling interest both to the general reader and the student eager to provide himself with a background for the scientific study of wood. The claim to be the oldest known tree on earth is made on behalf of a cypress-tree standing near Tule, in South Mexico. It has a circumference of 114 ft. and is 150 ft. high. Estimates as to its age vary from anywhere between five and ten thousand years, so it may well have been standing at the time of the building of the pyramids. Among the earliest records of timber usage are those pictures engraved on the walls of the temples and tombs of ancient Egypt dating from the days of the New Kingdom (1350 B.C.). A scene from the tomb of Nebamen at Thebes shows a carpenter seated on a stool and engaged in trimming to shape a balk of wood with an adze. From this and similar scenes we can gather that among the tools the Egyptian workmen used were large and small axes, adzes, chisels, and planes with files, to finish their work to a smooth surface. They were also provided with rulers, plummets, and right angles with which to set out their work. On the other hand, their method of sawing timber remained primitive owing to the fact that they used only handsaws, and never invented the long double-handled saw operated by two men. A tomb picture at Beny-Hassan enables us to see how the work was done. A man is using a deep handsaw, and the balk which he is sawing into boards is held upright between two posts fixed in the ground and joined at the top by a cross-bar, to which the balk is attached by cords. The operation of veneering was also practised by the Egyptians. Veneers thicker than those now used in the cabinet trade were hand-sawn from suitable decorative woods, covered with glue, and pressed down upon pine-core by means of weights or clamps. There are two pictures extant dating from the reign of Thothmes III (c. 1500 B.C.) showing the actual practice of the operations of veneering by craftsmen.   Also, as further evidence of this early veneering tradition, a number of pieces of Egyptian furniture have been recovered showing proof of veneering with coloured woods.   Several of these pictures, inscribed on stone as a living memorial of the first carpenters and joiners, have been copied from the walls of tombs and temples, and can be consulted by the reader at his leisure in the British Museum or in almost any good library.

Holy Scriptures tell us that Noah built the Ark of gopher wood, and that the length was 300 cubits, the breadth 50 cubits, the height 30 cubits.   The interior walls of the great Norman

DRAWINGS OF CHISELS, AUGERS, AND FILES FROM AN EGYPTIAN TOMB

From " Manners and Customs of the Ancient Egyptians" (British Museum).

cathedral of Monreale, outside the city of Palermo, in Sicily, are entirely covered with mosaics glittering in colours and gold, telling in picturesque detail the story of both the Old and New Testaments.   Among them, as will be seen from the frontispiece, is a lively composition showing " Noe " superintending his work-men in the building of the Ark.   This lifelike scene dates from the year A.D. 1182, and is particularly valuable to us as showing both the tools and methods of the medieval carpenter and joiner. For these Normans of Sicily were closely related to their brethren in England, and it is from the middle of the twelfth century that our story of the timber trade in England will start.   This picture is therefore worthy of close inspection.   It will be noticed that two men are sawing a log into planks.   For convenience one end of the log rests on a bank of earth, while the other is supported on a trestle so as to enable the ' bottom ' sawyer to work conveniently.   Now, this method of sawing endured for another seven hundred years—in fact, until the general adoption of sawmill machining in the middle of the nineteenth century. The sawyer standing in the ground was still known as the

Various Operations in Making the Pole and Other Wooden
Parts of a Chariot

(i) Sawing wood. (ii) Man seated shaping a pole with an adze. (iii) Bending poles.
(iv) (*Left*) A wooden chariot-yoke ; (*Right*) Wheelwrights assembling a wheel.
(After tomb-drawings at Thebes.)

British Museum.

'bottom' sawyer, and the whole practice as 'pitsawing,' from the depression or pit in which he worked ! Observe that the saw is held in a stiff wooden frame, so that both men can get a grip with both hands, and so put their full weight into the cut. In the final days of pitsawing of wood a saw with a single handle at each end was used, but who shall say it was as handy as its medieval counterpart ? Note the man sitting on top of the Ark, using a single-handled version of the great pitsaw to convert a smaller piece of timber into 'dimension' stock. The carpenter seen seated at the lower left-hand corner is using a hand-axe to chop out a mortice ; while his mate sitting astride a plank will be seen on close examination to be holding a short-handled tool with a cutting-head rather like a halberd. We know that medieval boats were clinker-built, and probably the shipwright is engaged in shaping the edge of the plank to make an overlap for the purpose of sheathing the side of the Ark. The mosaic gives a clear picture of the tools and methods of work of a medieval gang of carpenters and joiners from the moment of sawing the log into the necessary plank to finishing the various wooden parts ready to fit them into the Ark.

Another early story of the use of timber is the description in the Book of Chronicles of the building of the Temple by Solomon. The great King is said to have asked Hiram, King of Tyre, to send him cedar-trees, fir-trees, and algum- or almug-trees. The Bible gives alternative spellings of the last tree, and in one chapter we are told it is to come with the cedar and fir from Lebanon, while another gives its place of origin as Ophir. This latter land is thought to have been South-east Arabia, the country of the Queen of Sheba. The mention of two places of origin for the timber is to be explained by the fact that in any case it was the ships of Lebanon, the Phœnician trading kingdom of King Hiram, that brought the cargoes to King Solomon. Almug, or algum, wood was probably the Red Sandal Wood, and this is confirmed by the fact that it was used for such decorative purposes as the pillars and railings of the Temple, also for the making of harps and psalteries. The cedar-trees were to be obtained from the famous forests that once covered the mountains of Lebanon, and of which scattered areas survive to this day. The fir would have come from the same districts, and both must have provided first-class building and construction timber.

The early Greeks built their houses and temples entirely of wood, and when we come to the great stone temples of the classical Greek age it is clear that much of the construction design bears evidence of having been adapted from timber prototypes. It is said that the Greeks invented both the table and the bed, and, as can be seen from vase illustrations, they were accustomed to beautify their couches with decorative wood inlays. The Romans in their turn carried on the traditions of Greek art and technique. Woods were thinly sawn and applied to the surface of the furniture because they were specially figured or distinctively marked. Pliny's *Natural History*, Book 16, has a whole chapter on the art of veneering. The following quotation shows the type of woods preferred by the Roman cabinet-maker :

> The best woods for cutting into layers and employing as a veneer for covering others are the Citrus, the Terebinth, the various varieties of Maple . . . the root of the Elder and the Poplar.

The great naturalist Pliny also placed on record that trees were best felled in the last quarter of the moon, and more especially with the wind in the west, the best time of all being the last day of the winter solstice. This observation of Pliny's is extremely interesting, as it coincides exactly with the practice of the modern English timber merchant, who always fells his timber if possible in the middle of the winter.

It is by such glimpses into the past, helped by quotations from old records and extracts from contemporary writers, that we shall endeavour in the opening chapters of our book to build up a picture, or rather a series of tableaux, of the timber trade as practised in Great Britain from its early roots in medieval days to the present time. Then we shall deal with the history of the production of timber in three great exporting areas which have supplied the British market—namely, the Baltic area, the United States of America, and Canada, placing them in the order of historic priority, always remembering that the earliest settled areas of America included those largely wooded territories of Virginia and New England. After that we shall delve into the romantic stories of the three great staple hardwoods—mahogany, teak, and oak. Finally, we shall take a look into the past of a number of subjects closely related to timber, such as sawmilling, carpentry and joinery, wooden ships and shipbuilding, and also talk a little about the history of the use of timber in man's houses and homes.

Before starting on the historical journey as outlined above there are just a few timber trade terms, mainly relating to measurement, that should be explained, so as to put the general reader on equal terms with the student, and thus avoid reiteration and make the writer's task so much the easier. The basic unit of measurement in Great Britain, the Dominions, and Colonies is, and has been for a great number of years, the 'board foot of inch'—that is, the area of a piece of timber measuring twelve inches long by twelve inches wide by one inch thick. This unit is also known as the 'foot super of one inch,' so that one could equally well talk of a hundred board feet or a hundred feet super, according to one's inclination. After settling this basic unit of measurement, however, the great hardwood and softwood branches of the timber trade divide and go their own way as to larger units of measure. In the hardwood trade the next higher unit is a foot cube, which equals twelve board feet, so that, for example, one would be right in speaking of either two hundred and forty board feet or twenty cubic feet. Lastly, fifty feet cube make up one load. Now, in medieval times this word load had a literal meaning, being just that amount of wood that could be loaded on to a one-horse cart or wagon. It was only in later days, when measurements became exact, that the term 'load' was specified to equal exactly fifty feet cube.

The softwood trade, on the other hand, leaps straight away from the minimum unit of one board foot to the maximum unit of one standard, which equals 1980 board feet of one inch or feet super. Occasionally, however, the unit of a hundred board feet or feet super is used as a matter of convenience, particularly when sales are made of floorings or matchings. The standard unit of softwood has had a very varied career, and it was only as late as the second half of the nineteenth century that it was firmly fixed at 1980 feet super. Previous to that almost every port of shipment for softwood, whether in the Baltic or North America, had its own version of what comprised a standard of timber. The reader should be warned of one pitfall. In medieval documents one frequently finds records of timber sold by " the hundred." This term generally denoted a hundred pieces of timber, each twelve feet long by twelve inches wide, but on occasion the width would vary from nine inches to twelve inches. The term was used both in the case of hardwood, such as oak, or softwood, as fir. It was this 'hundred' that ultimately, as trade grew out of the Middle Ages into the spacious days of the sixteenth and seventeenth centuries, became the general fixed unit of measure now known as the standard, but only after many vicissitudes, as mentioned above. However, these matters will be gone into at greater length in due course in the appropriate chapters, when the reader will be initiated into the mysteries of the St Petersburg Standard, the Quebec Standard, and many another.

A number of countries on the metric system use metres and centimetres when making timber calculations for internal use, but when these metric countries export timber to the United Kingdom they commonly convert to the English measurement system for the benefit of their British customers. The British Colonies in North America naturally used the same system of measurements as the home country, and the United States of America to-day uses board measure, with the proviso that the American lumberman uses his own special method of calculating a board foot, quite naturally with the idea of saving time in the measurement of large quantities of sawn timber. The above remarks apply also to the Dominion of Canada. Timber intended for consumption in Great Britain is often sawn to the thicknesses of one inch and one inch and a quarter, which are both known as boards. This is the moment to draw attention to the fact that the trade symbol for an inch is written ", and for a foot is written ', so these two thicknesses would appear 1" and $1\frac{1}{4}$" respectively on documents, whereas if a board was twelve foot long the abbreviation would be 12'. Thicknesses above $1\frac{1}{4}$" are known as plank, and are usually supplied to the British market in the sizes of $1\frac{1}{2}$", 2", $2\frac{1}{2}$", 3", and 4", the trade symbol " being used in each case to denote an inch.

The reader will by now want a definition of the difference between hardwoods and softwoods. Generally speaking, from the point of view of the non-technical person, hardwoods are hard and softwoods are soft; there are, of course, exceptions to this common rule, for a number of hardwoods are softer than the hardest softwoods, and *vice versa*. Moreover, in Europe at any rate, but not in the tropics, hardwoods are deciduous—that is to say, they shed their leaves in the winter—while softwoods, with the exception of larch, are evergreens, and do not shed their leaves at any time of the year. The scientist will add that hardwoods belong to the broad-leaved family and softwoods to the narrow- or needle-leaved family. However, in case all this frightens the average reader, it is only necessary to reiterate what was said at the opening of the paragraph—namely, that generally speaking, hardwoods are hard and softwoods are soft, both to the feel and to work.

Readers can now feel that they are equipped with at any rate a basic knowledge of the timber trade's methods and terms of measurement sufficient for the purpose of this book. To delay any longer from embarking on our history would lay the author open to the criticism that a text-book is being put forward, instead of the fascinating story that it is hoped to unfold for their enjoyment.

CHAPTER II

THE MEDIEVAL TIMBER MERCHANT

TO build up the picture of the commencement of the timber trade in Great Britain the sources are the early Pipe Rolls, the Royal Exchequer Bills, and the Estate Rolls of the great feudal manors. It is a matter of interest that Pipe Rolls were so named because of the pipe-like appearance of the long, narrow parchment strips when rolled up and stored in racks. Each Roll carried the accounts of a whole year, every single item of disbursement being entered upon it. Fortunately there are still preserved many such documents showing in great detail the industrial payments to merchants, sub-contractors, and workmen. It is clear that for a century after the Norman Conquest (1066) there was very little timber trade as we understand the word trade to-day. All buildings of any size were erected by the King, the chief barons, or the Church. These great people provided for themselves the timber required by felling oaks and other trees from their own extensive woodlands to be sawn into balks and boards by pitsawyers on their own payrolls. There is, however, distinct evidence that in England by the middle of the twelfth century not only was the principle of the self-contained domains breaking down, but building was becoming more general. It was a time of the general loosening of strict feudal ties. Commerce expanded, and we witness the birth of the medieval timber trade.

It is from this time that Pipe Rolls and Estate Accounts, besides listing the wages of workmen employed on the estate or Royal Domain, begin to show items of so many trees, boards, or planks bought from such and such a person. In other words, the timber merchant makes his appearance on the scene ! These facts can be clearly demonstrated from a study of the Pipe Rolls of Windsor Castle, which are remarkably complete from its original foundation. In perusing what follows the reader is asked to bear in mind the great difference in the value of money as between the Middle Ages and to-day. In 1170 a charge of 19s. 10d. appears for boards sent from London by the Sheriffs

William Magnus and Edward Blundell, at Windsor. In 1252
the Sheriffs further sent 3000 Norway boards, with 50 great
boards especially for making tables, the whole consignment costing with carriage from London £19 4s. 6d. A few weeks later
2000 more Norway boards and 1000 lathes were demanded by
the Royal Master Carpenter and duly dispatched to Windsor.
A few years later, in 1260, the Sheriffs of London were directed
to dispatch at the request of one Alexander, described as the
King's Carpenter, 1000 boards for " Waynescoting " certain of
the King's rooms at the Castle, together with half a thousand
" Estrich " boards and half a hundred fir boards. It must be
understood that in all these transactions the Sheriffs were acting
ex officio, and were passing on the royal orders to the appropriate
timber merchants. The term " Estrich bordes " means boards
from the Eastern Reichs—*i.e.*, Norway, the Baltic countries, and
Prussia.

It is interesting to students of origins that up to 1250 or
thereabouts the word used in the medieval Latin (in which the
early Pipe Rolls are written) to denote partitioning or wainscoting
in any wood is " lambruscata." This is certainly a Latin translation of an early Norman French version of the modern French
lambris, equalling wainscot or ceiling. After 1250, however, the
word used in the Pipe Rolls for these purposes changes and
becomes " waynescote." This fact is an additional proof that
it was about the middle of the thirteenth century that Baltic
timber became a common article of commerce in this country.
Hence the word ' waynescote,' a rough-and-ready translation of
the German used by the Hanse merchants, who supplied the
timber, came into general use. The term ' waynescote ' is most
probably derived from the old German word ' wegen ' or
' wayne,' equalling wagon, together with ' schot,' equalling
partition. In medieval days large wagons were used for travelling, and were frequently partitioned as between passengers and
goods. The term originally applied to the partitioning of a
wagon subsequently became a trade name for all forms of wood
partitioning, including rooms, halls, libraries, etc. Later the
word ' waynescote ' came to be used to denote solely quartered
oak.

The old German derivation of these timber terms and others
to which we shall refer later brings us to the vital fact that

SAXON WOODEN CHURCH AT GREENSTEAD, NEAR ONGAR, ESSEX (*circa* 1015)
By courtesy of British Railways.

DETAIL SHOWING SPLIT OAK-TRUNK WALLS OF GREENSTEAD CHURCH
By courtesy of British Railways.

undoubtedly the activities of the merchants of the Hanseatic League, or Hanse, were largely instrumental in introducing fir and oak from the Baltic to England.   The Hanseatic League was a corporation of free towns granted special freedoms and trading privileges by the German Emperors from their Court at Aachen.   The leading cities were Hamburg, Utrecht, Bergen, Danzig, Wisby, Riga, and Lübeck.   At the latter a special tribunal sat to settle disputes between merchants and traders.   It was the custom of the merchants of the Hanse to export from the Baltic regions such raw materials as tallow, hides, fur, honey, and timber, while they sold to the local inhabitants in return manufactured articles of all descriptions, iron utensils, and Eastern spices.   This widespread trading corporation had by the middle of the thirteenth century acquired great power, and there is no doubt that the chief medium of exchange for Baltic timber was the famous English cloth which was freely exported from London and ports on the east coast to all parts of Northern Europe. Edward IV in the Treaty of Utrecht granted to the Hanseatic League a commodious office and residence in Thames Street. These were surrounded by a high wall and heavily fortified, owing to the jealous hatred of London traders.   All employees of the League lived behind these walls and were condemned to celibacy.   In those days trading connexions and channels were secrets of real value, to be carefully guarded with men's lives if necessary.   Members who broke the rules by marriage or associating with women were deprived of their membership of the Hanse and ignominiously expelled from their employment.   So strict were the rules that the male employees were not allowed lady visitors, even during the daytime, as it was feared that the fair sex would prise the League's treasured trade secrets from their swains.

In medieval times it was customary to lay a tax named ' Pontage ' upon certain commodities and articles to pay for the upkeep of bridges.   From the Patent Roll we learn that a Pontage for the repair of London Bridge was imposed in the year 1305, and that timber and staves were taxed as follows :

> Of every hundredth board of oak, coming from parts beyond the sea for sale, one halfpenny.   Of every hundredth of fir boards from beyond the seas for sale, twopence.   Of every twenty sheafs of wooden staves and arrow heads, for sale, one halfpenny.

Prospect der Mottlau von der Seite des Fisch-marckts nach dem Kuhin Thor
Prospectus Mottlaviae e regione fori pistarii versus Machinam, qua Molles in altum telluntur

THE PORT OF DANZIG, SHOWING THE WAREHOUSES OF THE HANSEATIC LEAGUE

Under the year 1273 there is an entry in the Account Roll of Norwich Cathedral Chapter as follows :

Delivered to John the Carpenter going to Hamburg to buy timber £14 ; to carriage of boards from Hamburg to Yarmouth £4.17.6d ; to carriage of the same boards from Yarmouth to Norwich 6s. od ; seven hundred of boards bought at Yarmouth £3.1.10d ; to carriage of same boards to Norwich 9d.

In 1293 it is recorded that the following goods were found on board eleven German ships driven by storms into Scarborough—namely, 20,060 fir boards and 300 bow staves.

Domesday Book, compiled in 1086, shows that Windsor was then a Royal Manor, and it was William the Conqueror who first built Windsor Castle as part of his policy to control the country. Henry I used the castle as a Royal Court, and married there his Queen Adeliza, daughter of the Duke of Louvain. Successive kings continued to improve both the defences of the castle and its amenities as a royal dwelling. King Edward III was born at Windsor Castle on November 13, 1312, and during his long reign of fifty years caused much building work to be done. In 1343 the King held at Windsor a great tournament, after which he decided to found an Order of Knighthood called the Round Table, after the traditional King Arthur. A building was actually constructed for their meeting-place. However, later the King changed his mind, and in 1348 founded the Most Noble Order of the Garter. He built for Canons and Clergy the College and Chapel, together with many other buildings, all of which exist to-day. Accordingly, the royal masons and carpenters were kept very busy during his reign. The following representative accounts are quoted from the Windsor Pipe Roll :

1314. For a thousand and half of lathes bought of Daniel the Ironmonger @ 5/10d. per thousand, 8s. 9d.

1345. Paid to John Losky [Losky is evidently not an English name] 100 Ringoldbolts bought for the stalls of the Chapel, £2.8.0.

1351. These boards, etc. were bought at the following intervals :

first week : 100 Ringoldbolts for the walls of the Chapel for 48s. and 50 Waynescot bords for the same walls for 7s. 6d.
second week : 60 Weynscotbords for 7s. 6d.
seventh week : 4 pieces of timber for 10s.

sixteenth week : half a hundred of Ryngoldbord for the Chapel stalls for 30s. and half a quarter of Estrich-bord for the same stalls, 4s.

thirty-first week : half a hundred of Ryngoldbord for the works of the said stalls for 20s. and the same quantity of Waynes-cotbord for the same stalls for 8s.

thirty-eighth week : a quarter of Ryngoldbord for the works of the said stalls for 13s., and a hundred of Waynescotbord for the same for 18s.

forty-seventh week : half a hundred of Estrich bord for the stalls for 8s.

1362. The appointment of John of Ashhurst to supply estrich bords, iron, nails and plaster of paris for the King's works at Windsor.

It is further recorded that in 1354 1000 " Estrich bords " were bought from one Foulko Horwode for the roof of a cloister for the sum of £9, while a certain John of Jondelay charged a further 10s. 10d. for barging the same by river from London to Windsor. In 1365 Richard Ballard and his fellows were paid 28s. 8d. for sawing 2150 feet of " Plaunches-bords " at 16s. per 100, while John Baker and his men got 33s. 8d. for sawing 250 Ryngoldbords. The time has now come to explain some of the terms in the above paragraphs. The word " Ryngoldbord " is derived from " Riga-board," Riga being then as now a con-siderable port of shipment for Baltic timbers. " Plaunches-bords " means planks or boards of wood dressed or planed ready for the joiner. In 1390 the Customs entries show that " Ryg-holts," " Waynescottes," " Barelholts," and " Deles " formed part of the cargo of the ship *Haricog* of Hamburg, unloading at Newcastle. This is an early mention of the traditional timber trade term ' deal.' It is undoubtedly an anglicized form of the Low German ' dele,' modern German *Diele*, both denoting sawn timbers and floorboards. The medieval word ' Barelholt ' means barelstave.

Regarding timber grown and produced in England, we have the following extract from the Windsor Pipe Rolls under the year 1352 :

1352. To John Coventre for 36 Elm boards price 4d. piece . . . .   12/8d.
To carriage of the same from London to Windsor. . .   5s.

To 60 Oaks bought of John atte Hall 12th January
for the Hall and Chambers in the Tower .... £13.6.8d.

And for 60 Oaks bought of the same John the 12th
day next following for the said works................ £10.0.0

And for 50 Oaks bought of the same John 10th
August for the said works......................... £6.5.0

And for 400 Oaks bought of Henry Sturmy for works
done within the said Castle .... £66.13.4d.

In 1365 William Parkhurst and his fellows were paid £6 5s. 6d.
for " scappling " 251 cartloads of timber in Shottesbrook Wood
at 6s. per load. " Scappling " is a medieval term denoting the
dressing of timber to size by means of an adze or axe—in other
words, rough-hewing. No doubt a lot of this work was done
on the oak used for the half-timbered halls and houses so prevalent
in medieval times.

The Chancery proceedings of the year 1400 record the complaint of Robert-atte-Wood and other English merchants for
imprisonment at Danzig. It appears that the Burghers of the
Hanse of that city tried to prevent the Englishmen from buying
" Waynescotes " and bow staves in the countryside, except
through their agency. It is tempting to surmise that Robert's
title rendered into modern English meant ' Robert at the Wood-
yard,' and, indeed, that probably was a fact. By an agreement
made between the Lord of Bergen and the merchants of London
in 1480 the sailors of Bergen were bound to close the hold and
hatches over " timber and other goods on pain of making good
damage caused by rain or seawater." Also if goods were injured
by rats the captain could escape responsibility if it was proved
that he had shipped a cat ! Then, as now, there were specialists
in the timber trade. In 1536 a certain Nicholas Hisham of York
had a licence from the King to sail to Prussia with four ships in
search of wood for spears and bows. It is recorded that this
trade was in the hands of the Nuremberg merchants, who held
a monopoly from the Emperor, Charles V.

The provision of yew staves for the famous English archers
was a continual preoccupation with the royal authorities. The
best staves came from abroad, being tough and elastic. Under
an Act of Richard III no wine was allowed to be imported from
Spain by ships' masters unless they also brought in their ships a
specified quota of yew for bow-making. We are told that in

1514 King Henry VIII " sent men of Science into Spain who chose 10,000 yew staves which were marked with the crown and rose and were the goodliest ever brought into England."

Among the ancient City Guilds or Companies of the City of London in existence to-day there are a Carpenters' and Joiners' Company and a Turners' Company. Once there was also a Company of Woodmongyres. This Company was unfortunately suppressed for misconduct in King Charles II's reign (1667), when its Charter was taken away because of extortion and other abuses. Mr Samuel Pepys writes in his diary that Sir George Downing, M.P., told him " that the thing that the House is just now upon is that of taking away the Charter from the Company of Woodmongyres, whose frauds it seems have been mightily laid before them." The " mysterie of the woodmongyres " is first mentioned in the year 1376, when a Common Council was formed from representatives of the Livery Companies to assist the Court of Aldermen in administering the affairs of the City of London. The first Hall of this Company stood in the area of the present Queen Victoria Street. Later the Woodmongers' Company established themselves in the buildings of the former Priory of Holy Trinity at Aldgate. This was a matter of convenience, as a wood market had existed in this district for several centuries. We hasten to add, however, that this Company of Woodmongyres consisted of firewood dealers, not of timber merchants ! In the days before the use of coal became general, firewood for fuel played a large part in the economy of the City of London.

CHAPTER III

THE DISCOVERY OF COLONIAL TIMBERS

THE Norwegians, it was said, warmed themselves comfortably by the Fire of London—an allusion to the large quantities of Norway fir that were imported for the reconstruction of the City after the disastrous Great Fire of London, which took place in 1666. Immediately the immense task of rebuilding London became urgent, and the Privy Council set up a special rebuilding Committee to deal with the situation. Among other things, this Committee was interested in the greatest possible substitution of Norway fir for oak, as it was considered that the domestic supplies of oak might be required in case of a naval emergency, the Dutch fleet then being very active. The records of this Committee show that they were informed on reliable evidence that " divers timber merchants are already buying up the timber in the country for the rebuilding of London." The same merchants are also mentioned as bringing Irish timber forward for this purpose, a certain Captain Nicoll being specifically listed as having imported two shiploads. The Navigation Acts were promptly relaxed so as to permit the greatest possible import of Eastland and Norwegian timber. In fact, on March 18, 1668, the Acts were entirely suspended as far as the importation to London of foreign timber and boards was concerned.

Samuel Pepys was Secretary to King Charles II's Navy, and as such had plenty of dealings with the timber merchants of his day. Pages of the famous diary show him as being continually preoccupied with the supply of suitable timbers and spars for the Navy. The three principal timber merchants with whom Samuel Pepys did business were Mr William Wood, Mr Castle, and Sir William Warren. Apparently Mr Castle specialized in wood from the British American Colonies, principally pine and fir from New England. Sir William Warren, on the other hand, was the great Baltic importer of his day. One of his contracts amounted to no fewer than 40,000 Scandinavian deals at £3 17s. per hundred. The timber was to be shipped from Gefle,

Swinsound, and Christiania. Sir William Warren had his timber-yard down the river at Deptford, and he took Mr Pepys on a visit there to show him his fine stock of deals, balks, spars, and masts. During the walk round the yards the Secretary was favoured with a lecture on how the Swedes felled and sawed their timber. The whole proceedings have an up-to-date appearance, because afterwards the pair adjourned to the office, where refreshments were served. Unfortunately insurance in those days was not the reliable business it is now. Sir William Warren's fine timber-yards were severely damaged by fire, and he died a poor man.

This is a convenient point to mention the early systems of measuring timber for sale. Samuel Pepys in his diary records that he was convinced that certain merchants selling oak logs to the Navy were not giving the King fair measure. He therefore enlisted the services of a young millwright, and after an early breakfast of eggs at the King's Head, Bow, took the young man into Epping Forest and persuaded him to show him the mystery of measuring trees by the " half square." Here is a quotation from the great diarist himself :

> August 18, 1662. About seven o'clock, took horse, and road to Bowe, and there staid at the Kings Head, and eat a breakfast of eggs, till Mr Deane of Woolwich and I rid into Waltham Forest, and there we saw many trees of the King's a-hewing, and he showed me the whole mystery of the half-square, wherein the King is abused in the timber that he buys, which I shall with much pleasure be able to correct. We rode to Ilford, and there, while dinner was getting ready, he and I practised measuring of the tables and other things, till I did understand measuring of timber and board very well.

To show what a painstaking man the Secretary was, he later informs us that after dinner that night he practised his newly acquired knowledge on his dining-room table. It is obvious that timber merchants and their customers must, from medieval times, have been much preoccupied with the problems of the measurement of both trees and squared timbers. It is probable that in the early days trees were bought for so much each. For instance, there is a record that in 1354 four elms were bought for King Edward III for the Works at Windsor for the sum of one shilling each. At that time oak timbers were recorded as being ought at so much per load, which then was an approximate measure only, being the amount of wood that could be placed on a one-horse cart.   It is not possible to ascertain exactly when the Hoppus system of measurement became generally adopted. Dr S. E. Wilson, however, writes that in his opinion the so-called Hoppus system was originally applied to the measurement of square logs.   He feels that, generally speaking, in medieval times trees were square-hewn by adze where they fell ; this practice would make their extraction easier, and also these hewn logs would be immediately ready for pitsawing into plank.   Later on, when the trade in round logs grew, the system was transferred to enable the carpenter to calculate what size square timber he would obtain from a given round log.   There is the further point that the medieval carpenter must have been equipped with some rudimentary calculations that would enable him to ascertain the point in the length at which a round log would have to be cross-cut so as to yield a beam of a desired square equal throughout to its whole length.   Although the Hoppus system did eventually exclude and drive out all other systems of round and square timber measurement, it was not, in fact, the earliest book of tables to be published.   What Mr E. Hoppus did was to improve and clarify the work of his predecessors.   The earliest Hoppus books in existence are copies of a second edition published in the year 1738 by the printer E. Wicksteed of London. It may be presumed that this second edition was preceded only a few years earlier by the first edition ; however, of this first edition no copies have come to light hitherto, and if any of my readers have the fortune to locate one it would be a matter of very great interest.   The fact is that John Darling, a mathematician living in Worcester, published a book in London in the year 1658 entitled *The Carpenter's Rule Made Easie*.   The title-page, set out below, is extremely interesting, as it would seem that Darling said that his system could be applied to other solid bodies besides timber :

> The Carpenter's Rule Made Easie, or The Art of Measuring Superficies and Solids as Timber, Stone, Board, Glasse and the like, it being of excellent use for Carpenters, Joyners, Masons, Glasiers, Painters, Sawyers, or any other that have occasion to buy or sell or make use of any such kinde of measure for themselves or others. Performed by certain Tables collected for that purpose by John

GENTLEMEN AND STEWARD DISCUSSING THE MEASURING OF A FELLED LOG
In the background is a forester felling a tree.
British Museum.

Darling. Printed by R. & W. Leybourn, for John Jones, Bookseller in Worcester, 1658.

It appears that Darling can really claim the honour of priority, as he makes no reference to any other tables besides his own, which, following the practice of others of that day, he certainly would have had they been in existence. Besides containing tables of measurement, the book was in the nature of a general instruction to the carpenter and his apprentice, and the contents page, as set out below, is most illuminating. Among the matters detailed are the following :

CONTENTS

The making of a two Foot Ruler.
The description and use of the Table of Board Measure.
A Table of the value of any number of feet of Board under an Hundred Foot, from 12 pence halfpenny the 100 Foot, to 20 shill. 10 pence the hundred foot.
A Table of the Fractional parts of a Foot of Board in the usual terms of quarters and half-quarters.
The Table of Board Measure.
Board-measure applied to Glasiers use.
The use of the Table of the Squaring of unequal-sided Timber.
A Table of the value of any number of Feet of Timber under 50 foot, from 12 pence half-penny 50 foot price, to 20 shill. 10 pence 50 foot price.
Common Errours in measuring of Timber.
The Table of the Fractional parts of a Foot of Timber in the usual terms of quarters and half-quarters.
The description and use of the Table of Timber-Measure.
The Table of Timber-Measure.
The description and use of the Table of Multiplication.
Further use of the Table of Multiplication joyned with the Table of Board-measure.
The Table of Multiplication.

Another system was that known as *Keay's Practical Measurer*. A copy of this is in existence, dated 1724. From the preamble to this work it is evident that in the number of years intervening since Darling's first publication a number of methods had come into being, and that there was considerable controversy between the exponents of the various schools. To return to Hoppus, it is noteworthy that the preface to his second edition of 1738 contains the following words :

> Besides the contents given by this new method, I have likewise set down the contents of each tree as given by Keay and Darling to show that this method is more intelligible and better suited to ordinary capacity than either of the others.

He also gives his guarantee that his system is correct, and refers to the intolerable blunders and numerous imperfections with which other tables already existing for the measuring of timber and stone abound. This is not the place to give a full explanation of the Hoppus system of measurement, and the reader may be referred to *Decimal Hoppus Tables*, by Dr S. E. Wilson, published by the Arbor Press. Briefly put, however, the unit of quantity is the Hoppus foot, for which the formula is as follows :

$$\text{Hoppus feet} = \frac{\left(\dfrac{\text{girth in inches}}{4}\right)^2 \times \text{length in feet}}{144}.$$

A quarter-girth tape, upon which statutory inches are marked as quarter-inches, is used and placed round the middle of the desired tree so that the girth may be taken, and the resultant cubic measurement is then obtained from the tables. A tree that regularly tapers from butt to top is usually measured in one length. Where the regular growth of a tree has been broken by large boughs, etc., it is customary to measure it in several well-marked sections. The buyer and seller usually agree together as to how much of the total length of the felled tree shall be taken as merchantable timber.

John Evelyn, the diarist and naturalist, born in 1620 and educated at Balliol College, Oxford, friend of Samuel Pepys, published in 1664 his famous book *Sylva* under the auspices of the recently founded Royal Society. The book was based upon a discourse which was written at the request of the Royal Society to answer certain queries propounded to them by the principal officers and Commissioners of the Navy in relation to the proper methods of forestry and the felling of trees for the provision of timber to His Majesty's Navy. We cannot do better than round

off our discussion on timber-measuring by quoting John Evelyn
from his book *Sylva* :

> Every person who can measure timber thinks himself qualified
> to value standing trees ; but such men are often deceived in their

THE CABINET-MAKER ENJOYING HIS TIPPLING TIME
From an engraving by J. F. Martin, 1779.

estimates. It is the perfect knowledge of the application of the
different shaped trees that enables a man to be correct in his valuation. A foot of wood may be of little value to one trade, but of
great value to another. This is the grand secret which enriches the
purchasers of standing timber.

This statement of Evelyn's is equally true to-day. Since the year of its first publication in 1664 John Evelyn's notable book has seen many editions, and is to-day regarded as a monument to both literature and the practice of forestry.

It is now time for us to investigate the early developments of the Colonial timber trade. The seventeenth-century imports consist of Spanish Mahogany (so called from its being imported originally from the Spanish Colonies), walnut, coromandel, rosewood, and amboyna. These fine woods were employed in their full beauty in the next century by hosts of Georgian cabinet-makers, among whom the most famous were Thomas Chippendale (1718–79), George Hepplewhite (d. 1786), Richard Gillow (1740–1811), and the great furniture designer Thomas Sheraton (1751–1806). The earliest known use of mahogany is a cross still preserved in the Cathedral of San Domingo (West Indies), and bearing the date 1514. There is an original bill in existence showing that a number of rooms in Nottingham Castle were panelled in 1680 with mahogany or cedar-wood. In the *London Gazette* dated February 22, 1702, there is an advertisement for " Mohogany Wood " for sale as part of the cargoes of two prize ships taken from the Spaniards. It would appear that the original use of mahogany was for shipbuilding, but in England from the year 1715 the wood was employed for tables, chairs, and other furniture. By that date sufficient stocks of this handsome timber had accumulated in the hands of the timber merchants of London and other principal ports for it to become generally available to cabinet-makers. It is said that mahogany was greatly admired by the beautiful Duchess of Buckingham, and she did much to establish the fashion.

In 1774 a *History of Jamaica* was published, in which it was stated that mahogany formed one of the largest exports from the island to Great Britain, the shipments being composed partly of large quantities of planks and squared timbers brought to Jamaica from the Spanish colonies on the mainland, to be shipped subsequently to importers in Great Britain. Sheraton's *Cabinet Dictionary*, published in 1803, mentions already three varieties of mahogany under the names of Cuba, Spanish, and Honduras. Of these he says that the Spanish wood is the finest, while he informs us that Cuba Mahogany was chiefly employed for chair-making. We are told that Honduras Mahogany, sometimes known as Baywood, was also much esteemed by cabinet-makers.

The time has now come to survey the state of the English timber trade from the point of view of home production. A survey of the New Forest was made in 1608, and registered 123,927 trees as being likely to be suitable for Navy use. The wars of the seventeenth century, however, had a disastrous effect upon this famous forest, as by 1707 the Navy Surveyors could report only 12,476 as fit for their use. It must be borne in mind that it was estimated then that a single ship of the line required for her construction the product of no fewer than 4000 well-grown oak-trees—let us say, 150,000 ft. cube of timber. Near London the Crown forest of Hainault had been reduced by encroachment to less than 3000 acres. In a survey of 1783 it was stated that there were standing only some 11,055 oak-trees, of which only 2760 were of Navy grade and size. There is no doubt that from the days of Queen Elizabeth onward the vast growth of not only the Royal Navy, but also the Mercantile Navy, had eaten deeply into Britain's forests. Up to the seventeenth century Great Britain had been mainly a country of hardwood forests and woods. The few softwood trees found up to that time had been virtually intruders. It was not until the following century that the nobility and country gentlemen commenced to make plantations of fir and pine on a large scale. In Scotland by the end of the eighteenth century the establishment of softwood plantations was in full swing : not only fir and pine were being planted, but also varieties of spruce and larch. Already by the end of the eighteenth century these woodlands were being exploited on a commercial basis. Meidinger, the German forester and a great admirer of England, in his well-known work, states :

> In Garmouth at the mouth of the River Spey stood a number of sawmills rented by the Duke of Gordon to the London Timber Company. Here the timber floated down the river from the forest of Badenoch, was cut up and shipped by sea to London, mainly to Deptford and Woolwich.

This is a convenient moment to take a look at the birth of the sawmiller. The earliest sawmills were set up in the Baltic countries as early as the sixteenth century. One of the earliest mills is said to have been established in Norway in 1530. The

MAHOGANY-TREES IN THE WEST INDIES

"*Illustrated London News*," *April 6, 1850.*

Dutch were early in the field, and a mill for sawing wood was erected at Saadam in 1596. Crude reciprocating saws were employed, set up in wooden frames, driven by wind- or water-power. Partly owing to the objections of the pitsawyers, power-driven sawmill machinery was a late arrival in England. In 1761 the Royal Society of Arts awarded a premium to James Stanfield amounting to £300 for a plan for a sawmill. Charles Dingley, to whom Stanfield was introduced by the Royal Society of Arts, actually built the sawmill at Limehouse. The motive-power was supplied by wind-vanes, but unfortunately shortly afterwards the sawmill was burnt to the ground by a crowd of pitsawyers, who feared for their livelihood. It was Samuel Bentham, Inspector-General of Naval Works, who actually pioneered sawmilling in Great Britain. The Government in 1779 sent him to make a tour of the Baltic countries to report on the progress of woodworking and shipbuilding. Shortly after his return to England in 1791 he patented a planing machine for wood. Later he went into partnership with his brother, Jeremy, and between 1791 and 1795 invented various other sawmilling machines.

To show the comprehensive stock of the timber importer in the middle of the eighteenth century, Campbell, in his *London Tradesmen*, published in 1747, states that a London timber merchant was " furnished with deal from Norway, either in logs or plank ; with Oak and Wainscoat from Sweden and some from the Counties in England ; with Mahogany from Jamaica ; with Wallnut tree from Spain." Moreover, fortunately for us, Mr Henry Warburton, M.P., before a Select Committee of the House of Commons sitting in 1835, gave an almost verbatim report of the working of a Georgian yardkeeper's business. He opened his evidence as follows :

> In the year 1808, on my father's death, I succeeded him in his business, which was that of a wholesale dealer in foreign timber, commonly known to the timber trade in London by the name of " a yard keeper." I continued in that business from 1808 until the end of the year 1831, when I quitted it. The nature of it was to obtain foreign timber for sale, either by purchasing in the home market of the importer, or (when I found it to my advantage) by importing it myself. Besides the information I acquired from my own experience, I have that to be obtained from the books of my

father, and of his predecessors in the same business, which extend
from 1757 down to 1808.

   This is a very interesting sidelight on the methods of conducting the early timber trade of London, showing as it does that
the term ' yard-keeper ' was already in use in 1757. It also shows
that at that time there was already a differentiation between importers and yard-keepers ! Later on Mr Warburton told the
Committee that in the second half of the eighteenth century the
merchants who imported from Norway acted principally as
consignees for cargoes forwarded by the Norwegian mill-owners.
These the merchants sold without the intervention of the broker
or yard-keeper. The yard-keeper on landing his Norwegian
goods sorted them for himself into two qualities—namely, best
and second—and paid for them to the Norwegian shippers according to his own grading—a very happy state of affairs ! One
month was the time allowed for the landing and sorting of
cargoes. At the end of that time a bill at six months' date was
drawn on the yard-keeper subject to a discount of $2\frac{1}{2}$ per cent.
and accepted by him for the cargo. On the other hand, there
were some merchant bankers interested principally in the iron
trade who also occasionally imported timber from Sweden,
Russia, and the Baltic ports, and these cargoes were sold generally
through a broker, who received a commission of 1 per cent.
In this case the yard-keeper accepted bills at four months. Here
is a direct quotation from the evidence of Mr Warburton :

   Almost the whole of the deals and timber at that time imported
   into London and used by consumers other than the Government
   were sold to the yard keepers in the first instance, they being the
   wholesale dealers through whom carpenters, building and other
   consumers were supplied. The yard keepers rarely imported to any
   considerable extent except in the case of some particular goods. On
   the other hand the Merchant importers and the Brokers abstained
   from selling directly to consumers, apprehensive of losing the favourable regard of the yard keepers by interfering with their business.

He later told the Committee that the establishment of bonded
docks opened to the merchant-importer such facilities for trading
with the consumer direct that the old usage of keeping these
two parties asunder was greatly broken down. These bonded
docks enabled the importer to warehouse his goods, preserve
them for use until dry, and deliver the whole or part of a cargo

to a customer without having recourse to the yard-keeper. The
granting, therefore, to public companies of bonding on the one

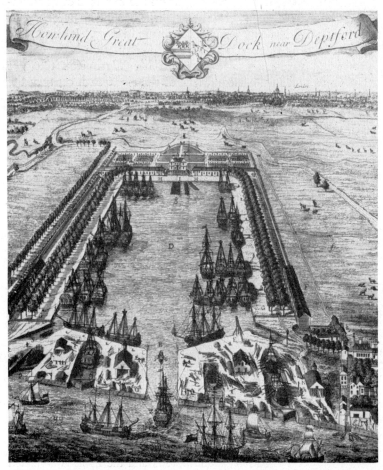

HOWLAND GREAT DOCK, NEAR DEPTFORD, IN THE REIGN OF HENRY VIII
By courtesy of the Parker Gallery, 2 Albemarle Street, London W.1.

hand, and the withholding from the yard-keeper the privilege
of doing the same on their own premises on the other hand, had
the effect of transferring the larger share of the business of
directly supplying the consumer from the yard-keeper to the
merchant-importer. Before parting with this worthy gentleman

I must give you his answer to the following question put to him in examination. He was asked, " Is timber an article like wine that benefits from keeping ? " He replied, " If the question refers to timber in the log, owing to its becoming shaken by the weather, it sells for 15 per cent. less the second year than the first, and so for less and less the longer you keep it. On the other hand, as to deals, at the end of eighteen months from the time of importation they are scarcely dry enough for the consumer's use."

It is not generally known that by the end of the eighteenth century Great Britain was importing a very large percentage of her total timber consumption. Concerning the industrial history of this period, a famous historian has written : " Among the regular British imports there was one true bulk trade and one only—the timber trade." In 1790 this country imported close upon 200,000 loads of fir timber from Northern Europe alone. In 1831 700,000 loads of timber of all sorts, both hardwood and softwood, passed the Customs. By 1845 this figure had risen to 1,300,000 loads, to reach no less a grand total than two million loads in 1846. Up to 1800 the quantity of softwoods coming from North America was almost negligible, but the old adage that history repeats itself may well be quoted, because the effect of war upon British economy does not change whether the battle takes place in the eighteenth or twentieth century !

This can be said advisedly, because the fear of a timber famine when Napoleon enforced his famous " Continental System " upon Europe from 1809 onward effected a revolution in the timber trade of the United Kingdom. By 1821 the Colonial imports, which, as mentioned above, had been small, were nearly three times that of the foreign. The Government did its best to encourage this state of affairs by raising the duty on Baltic deals, etc., from 6s. 8d. a load or ton in 1793 to 65s. in 1819, Colonial timbers being admitted either free or with a very small tax. This so changed conditions that by 1821 it was said that Baltic timber was employed only in the more valuable description of buildings. A witness to the aforementioned Select Committee, Mr John Armstrong, was asked about a visit he had paid to Dutch timber-yards in 1820, and replied :

I did not observe any deals of the same specification as we import in this country. I found logs of amazing length cut out, some into slabs of various thicknesses, others into pieces of 18" square, 40 feet long, from immense sized trees ; they had been cut dry and perfectly clean. I said to a Dutch timber merchant : " I should very much like to have some of this wood in London, it is so superior to what we are in the habit of receiving, how do you get it ? " The Dutchman replied, " We get it down the river Rhine."

It would appear that this fine timber must have been pine from the Black Forest.

Further evidence was given that Christiania deals, from Norway, were considered the best import at the end of the eighteenth century. Yellow deals were used for all outside work ; the witness said that they never thought of using white for out- side work, because it was not so durable, being " deprived of turpentine." White deals were used for internal fittings, such as doors and dados, skirtings and window-shutters. Before the Select Committee witnesses were questioned closely on the re- spective merits of American and Baltic deals Sir Robert Smirke, a builder, said of American deals, " I rarely see them in London, nor do I use much of American red wood in London on account of the prejudice which exists against it. On the other hand, in the north-western parts of England, and in Scotland particularly, it is difficult to get any other wood but the American. I have seen some very handsome floors made of American red wood." American or Canadian Yellow Pine was, of course, largely used both for door and joinery purposes in Regency houses. Sir Robert Smirke was also questioned about the increasing use of iron. A member of the Committee asked if it was not due to the greatly increased price of timber during the Napoleonic Wars, and inquired if it had supplanted Baltic timber in the construction of roofs. Sir Robert replied, " Yes ; the whole of some roofs are of iron. I made all that of Lord Somers' house, Eastnor Castle, in iron, except the lathes, which were laid to receive the slates. The principal part of the floor and roofs of the Museum are also of iron." He further said that Lord Somers' house was begun in 1812, and was one of the first private houses in which iron was used. Talk of the use of substitutes for timber had been common for some years, but surely this instance of the use of iron in 1812 is one of the earliest ? The following table gives a clear picture of the drastic

SHIPS UNLOADING TIMBER BALKS IN THE RIVER THAMES AT THE CLOSE OF THE EIGHTEENTH CENTURY

From a print in the collection of the Port of London Authority.

change forced upon the timber trade of Great Britain by the
Napoleonic Wars :

	AVERAGE QUANTITIES IN EACH PERIOD			PERCENTAGE PROPORTION OF COLONIAL
PERIODS OF FIVE YEARS EACH	From the Baltic	From the British N. American Colonies	Total	
	stds.	stds.	stds.	
1. From 1788 to 1792 .	73,132	866	74,019	1
2. „ 1793 „ 1797 .	54,866	408	55,275	1
3. „ 1798 „ 1802 .	59,336	972	60,311	1
4. „ 1803 „ 1807 .	77,392	5,511	83,003	6
5. „ 1808 „ 1812 .	24,572	40,179	64,751	62
6. „ 1814 „ 1818 .	41,951	49,199	91,151	54
7. „ 1819 „ 1823 .	38,866	111,851	150,719	74
8. „ 1824 „ 1828 .	63,963	136,967	200,931	68
9. „ 1829 „ 1833 .	40,927	134,227	178,488	76

During the early part of the eighteenth century the principal
timber shipping ports of Norway were Dram, Krageroe, Long-
sound, and Porsground. These ports specialized in deals from
$1\frac{1}{2}''$ to $2''$ thick and 9 ft. to 16 ft. long. Other Norwegian ports
were Christiania, Frederickstadt, Moss, and Larwig. These latter
cut their Red Wood deals mostly to $1\frac{1}{4}''$ and $2\frac{1}{2}''$, 9 ft. to 13 ft.
long, and their White Wood to $3''$ deals of the same length. The
reason for the popularity of $1\frac{1}{4}''$ material was that in those days
it was the proper thickness for flooring-boards. The fact is that
up to the close of the eighteenth century it was the Norwegian
forests which supplied by far the greater proportion of the Scandinavian softwoods exported to Great Britain. Up to that time the
Swedish shipments were quite small, and it was only after the
Napoleonic Wars that Sweden moved to her prior position as exporter. Stockholm was originally the principal port of shipment.

To turn now from Scandinavia to the ports of the Baltic,
it appears that the timber shipped from Danzig during the
eighteenth century was almost entirely deck-plank for shipping.
We are told that a typical specification would be 40 ft. long $\times$ $12''$
wide $\times$ $3''$ thick. Such sizes are, of course, unheard of to-day.
From Memel came red deals and battens mostly in the thicknesses
of $1\frac{1}{2}''$, $2''$, and $2\frac{1}{2}''$. Readers may have noticed very red roof-
timbers and rafters in Regency houses, and these would be wood

from Danzig and Memel, both their redness and hard-wearing qualities being due to the turpentine in the wood. It is probably not generally realized that the importation of Russian wood cargoes into this country commenced as early as 1700. St Petersburg (Leningrad), Naron, Wyborg, and Onega were the principal Russian ports of shipment. Many of the cargoes carried large quantities of $1\frac{1}{2}''$ plank in the widths of 9″ and 11″. This was due to the fact that there was a great demand in the eighteenth century for $1\frac{1}{2}''$ Red Wood boards clear of all knots and defects for the manufacture of the great deal staircases that graced the Regency houses. Shipments from the northerly port of Archangel also commenced to arrive about this time, mostly in the form of $2\frac{1}{2}''$ and 3″ deals.

As mentioned earlier, the outbreak of the Napoleonic Wars entirely changed for the time being the source of the country's timber imports, Great Britain being almost totally cut off from the traditional Baltic sources of supply. The timber merchants, encouraged by the Government both by exhortation and the easing of Customs duties, turned to North America, principally the newly won territory of the Canadas. From a pamphlet entitled *A Reply to the Observations of a British Timber Merchant on the Report of the Select Committee of the House of Lords relative to the Timber Trade*, published in London in the year 1821 by an anonymous " Merchant," we learn that the timber exports from the North American colonies—*i.e.*, territories now comprised in the Dominion of Canada—for the five years period from 1815 to 1819 were as follows :

Years	Fir Timber Loads	Oak and Oak-plk. Loads	Masts under 12″ Dia.	Masts above 12″	Deals and Deal Ends	Battens and Ends	Staves	Wscts. Logs Loads
1815	107,550	3,424	4,696	3,231	1,913	53	12,914	14
1816	131,825	6,522	4,746	6,354	1,702	93	21,025	—
1817	140,280	4,320	5,252	7,983	3,471	201	23,743	—
1818	214,102	4,725	6,729	4,263	6,481	250	33,046	—
1819	267,065	9,483	9,170	5,002	9,871	359	42,098	—
Total .	860,822	28,474	30,593	26,833	23,438	956	132,826	14
Average	172,164	5,695	6,118	5,336	4,687	191	26,565	3

This pamphlet draws our attention to the fact that following upon the close of the Napoleonic Wars considerable agitation took place among timber merchants, especially on the part of those who had been accustomed to import Baltic softwoods and who now found themselves, although the wars were over, still badly placed for business owing to the heavy duties still imposed upon Swedish and other Baltic softwoods in comparison with the light ones laid upon Canadian imports.   Consequently, a number of Committees were established by the Government from time to time to consider these matters and take evidence. In particular a Select Committee of the House of Commons reported in the year 1835. This is a voluminous document, and much interesting information can be obtained as to how the British timber trade was conducted in the preceding fifty years. This House of Commons Committee recommended a considerable measure of equalization of the duties, although all duties on timber were not finally abolished until the year 1866.

In the library of Mr T. A. Storey, past Chairman of the Timber Development Association, is a price-list of timber issued by Messrs Dempsey and Picard, Greenland Street, Queen's Dock, Liverpool, bearing the date 1821. This very interesting document shows clearly what a complicated affair the softwood market was at the beginning of the nineteenth century. No fewer than six columns were required to deal with the following points. First a description of the wood, followed by a column for prices, then comes an account of the duties incurred, followed by two columns for goods shipped in British bottoms and/or those in foreign bottoms respectively, the duties on the latter being considerably heavier.   Last of all there are remarks on quality, specification, etc. As mentioned earlier, this old price-list brings out clearly the fact that at this time it was the wood from British America which was the cheapest, and consequently in greatest demand.   Quebec deals were selling at £14 to £16 per standard hundred with very little duty imposed upon them.   On the other hand, Archangel and Petersburg Red were selling at £18 10s. per standard hundred, Danzig Red at £15, Swedish and Finnish at £17, with Gothenburg and Sundswald at £16 10s. per standard hundred, all plus duty in the neighbourhood of £20 per standard hundred.

We are indebted to Messrs Edward Chaloner and Co. for a

copy of a report issued by them at Liverpool on February 6, 1823. The importation of Spanish Mahogany is stated to have amounted to 2750 logs for the year, and prices at auction ranged from 10*d*. to 2*s*. 3*d*. per foot. There was also an importation of 903 logs from Honduras. A small quantity of Wainscot oak logs was received from the Baltic—namely, 350. A special mention is made of African Oak, known to us now as Iroko ; 30,000 cubic feet were received during the year under review. The demand, we are told, was principally for shipbuilding and canal work. It is clear that African Oak was imported from the West Coast of Africa long before African Mahogany—now the prime favourite from those areas—was exploited commercially. No doubt during the great shipbuilding programmes of the first decade of the nineteenth century the British Admiralty was continually searching for new sources of timber suitable for use in H.M. dockyards.

CHAPTER IV

THE NINETEENTH CENTURY ONWARD

OUR survey now reaches the time which saw the birth of a number of timber firms carrying on trade to-day. Here are some of the names and dates. Situate in London : Mr Christopher Gabriel founded in 1770 the business of Messrs Gabriel and Sons, now amalgamated into the well-known firm of Gabriel, Wade, and English, Ltd ; Churchill and Sim, Ltd, 1813 ; J. J. and S. W. Chalk, 1814 ; William Oliver and Sons, Ltd, 1815 ; C. Leary and Co. (under the title of Skeen and Leary), 1841 ; Samuel Putney, Ltd, 1846 ; Wm. Marshall and Son, Ltd, 1851 ; Bambergers, Ltd, 1851 ; John Wright and Sons (Veneers), Ltd, 1866 ; Price and Pierce, Ltd, 1869 ; W. W. Howard Bros. and Co., Ltd, 1876 ; William Mallinson and Sons, Ltd, 1877 ; James Latham, Ltd, founded in Lancashire in 1757 and established in London in 1815. The business of Messrs Jarratt, Pyrah, and Armitage, Ltd, of Huddersfield, was originally established by Mr William Lucas in 1774, and after a very interesting history the present owners acquired the business in 1919. In Liverpool : Messrs Joseph Gardner and Sons, Ltd, 1748 ; Edward Chaloner and Co. (Timber), Ltd, 1820 ; Duncan Ewing and Co., Ltd, 1830 ; James Webster and Bro., Ltd, 1862 ; Robert Cox and Co., 1865. In other towns : Messrs John Sadd and Sons, Ltd, Maldon, 1767 ; John Stenning and Son, East Grinstead, 1792 ; Jewson and Sons, Ltd, Norwich, 1836 ; Edmiston and Mitchells, Glasgow, 1845 ; E. Longhurst and Sons, Epsom, 1873.

The West India Docks opened for business on August 2, 1802. Commodious sheds were built, and by the middle of the nineteenth century the docks had become a centre of the hardwood importing trade. Here the various firms of timber brokers handled the parcels of mahogany logs which were consigned to them continuously from Honduras, Cuba, Costa Rica, San Domingo, etc. An idea of the strenuous nature of those days may be gathered from the fact that the sales were mainly held at six o'clock in the evening. The logs had been valued the preceding day by merchants wearing the tight morning coats and stove-pipe hats of those days. The actual sale would be held in a coffee-house such as the famous Lloyd's or Garraway's. These establishments maintained well-furnished public rooms to which merchants would resort not only to drink coffee, but also to discuss business with their agents and to garner the commercial intelligence from the newspapers of the day.

A catalogue of a sale by Messrs C. Leary is in existence dated Tuesday, February 24, 1852, for the sale by auction at Garraway's Coffee-house, Cornhill, of two cargoes of San Domingo Mahogany per *Presto* (Captain Ellis) and *Penelope* (Captain Renwick). Altogether there were put up for auction on this occasion 976 logs of San Domingo Mahogany, 17 logs of Pencil Cedar, and 225 logs and planks of Rio Rosewood. The lots were sold by candle, " the highest bidder in time to be the Buyer." It is interesting to see this practice of selling " by the candle" enduring into the middle of the nineteenth century. The method was for a short piece of candle to be lit as the lot was put up for sale, and the highest bidder before the candle expired would be declared the buyer by the auctioneer. Prices in this catalogue ranged from 5*d*. to 20*d*. per foot. The names of the bidders and the prices paid were all written in by the owner of the catalogue (James Latham, who owned a house and timber-yard at 124 Curtain Road, London, E.C.), plus a very human note against one lot—" Will you take 5 per cent. on your cost ? "— showing that the commercial instincts of those days were well developed, and merchant-to-merchant trading is no new thing !

We are once again indebted to Messrs Chaloner for a number of other trade documents relating to the middle of the nineteenth century. The firm's catalogue for Wednesday, February 2, 1848, is still preserved, and is in the form of a booklet with a preface stressing the great advantage of Liverpool to the country buyer. We cannot do better than quote verbatim :

> The distant buyer cannot be too often reminded of the benefit which he derives by laying in his stock of mahogany and other choice woods at Liverpool. To this depot of the richest cabinet-making woods, the most adventurous, persevering and experienced of the importers now undeviatingly destine the fruits of their speculations, and through their rivalry we are enabled to bring forward a vast amount of mottled and roey table wood, besides

ranges of the most superb veneer pieces, both logs and curls, and present, for the continental markets also, more than an ordinary supply for exportation. This port offers to the buyer great advantages in the mode of measurement, and it cannot be too often repeated that every third log—reckoned by the customs' caliper, is allowed as a tare or draft, agreeably with an established usage peculiar to Liverpool.

This last statement presumably is a reference to the custom of Liverpool Measure. This measurement system (consolidated towards the end of the nineteenth century) granted to the buyer of mahogany logs a rebate of $1\frac{1}{2}''$ in every $12''$—in other words, payment was made for only $10\frac{1}{2}''$ out of every foot. This practice no longer exists, having been abolished during the days of the Timber Control in the Second World War. No doubt it was a survival of those days when it was customary for the overseas shipper of logs to make large allowances in measure, both to compensate the buyer for faults and also to meet the waste involved in sawmilling. Apparently in early days, contrary to the practice in London of adjourning to the comfort of a coffee-house, the logs were actually sold on the Liverpool quays, the auctioneer moving with the buyers from lot to lot. In fact, in a copy of the *Illustrated London News* dated April 6, 1850, there is an illustration [1] of an enormous Honduras Mahogany log sold in the sheds at Birkenhead Docks by the brokers, Messrs Holmes, Salter, and Crook. The log is described as being about 6 ft. square and 20 ft. long. The auctioneer is standing on top of it, and is in the act of knocking the lot down for 1s. $10\frac{1}{2}d$. per ft. super with his walking-stick. Around stand an appreciative circle of buyers, which, we are told, numbered about 160. The buyers are shown as wearing the typical Victorian garb, and their considerable number shows the importance which these Liverpool mahogany sales had already reached.

Another catalogue and market report of Messrs E. Chaloner and Co. is dated February 3, 1865. The front page gives details of the goods to be sold that day. They consisted of "Pine and Spruce Deals just landed ex 'Golden Pledge' from St John, New Brunswick." It is noteworthy that the preamble says that "these goods will be sold at twelve o'clock at noon precisely on the Quay of Egerton Dock at Liverpool." There is no

[1] See p. 170.

mention of the comfort of a saleroom, and one could imagine that the 3rd of February at Liverpool might be quite a chilly day.

The Quebec trade must have been very brisk in those days, as the following quantities of various timbers listed as having been brought into Liverpool indicate : Quebec Red Pine 527,499 ft. cube and Quebec and United States Oak 1,180,634 ft. cube were received during the year. We are told that an immense demand for this oak sprang up, principally for railway-wagon work. The logs averaged from 2s. 3d. to 2s. 6d. per ft. cube according to quality. In addition 267,118 ft. cube Quebec Elm was received, and 17,927 ft. cube of Quebec Ash.

The market report on the back of the catalogue shows the range of decorative fancy woods dealt in by Liverpool importers in the year 1864 to be remarkable. Their variety is equalled only by their cheapness. Mahogany is featured in four varieties— St Domingo at 1s. to 2s. per ft. super ; Cuba at 7d. to 1s. ; Honduras from 5½d. to 7d., and Mexican from 5d. to 7d. per ft. super. Satinwood from St Domingo figures at from 1s. to 1s. 6d., while Italian Walnut could be purchased at the extremely low figure of 4s. per ft. cube. Bird's Eye Maple at 3d. to 6d. per ft. super of 1″ also appears cheap. Other decorative woods which are listed are Zebrawood, Crocus wood, Partridge wood, Tulip wood, Lettuce wood, Rosewood, and Ebony. Among constructional timbers are Pitch Pine logs from Savannah and Charleston at 4s. 6d. per ft. cube, Greenheart at 3s. 6d. per ft. cube, Sabicu at 3s. 6d., and Black Morra at 2s. 6d. per ft. cube. Another interesting entry is for East India Teak logs at 5s. per ft. cube, with 2″ Teak plank at 8d. to 1s. per ft. super. If these planks were native-sawn they must have been the early product of an Indian or Burmese sawmill. Under the heading of Baltic woods is listed an item of the famous Crown Wainscots from the port of Riga in the shape of solid logs sold Queen's Calliper Measure at from 4s. 6d. to 6s. 6d. per ft. cube. An interesting point is that only two lengths are specified—i.e., 7 ft. and 14 ft. Evidently these Wainscots were imported especially for the coffin trade. Readers engaged in the stave trade will be attracted by the following entries : Danzig and Memel Crown Pipe per 1200 pieces—250 shillings ; Trieste Pipe Staves per 1200 pieces— 230 shillings ; Hogshead ditto—35 shillings ; Barrel ditto—28 shillings. These latter were evidently from the famous Austrian

Oak forests.   United States White Oak Staves fetched less—
Pipes 100s. per 1000 and Barrels 12s. per 1000 staves.

These were the days when mahogany was truly king in
Liverpool.   Beautiful logs of exceptionally large dimensions,
many of them finely figured, flowed into the famous port in a
continuous stream from all parts of tropical America and the
West Indies.   The final abolition of all duties on timber in 1866,
which event had followed the repeal of Colonial Preference a
few years earlier, heralded revolutionary changes in the softwood
branch of the timber trade.   To take the position at home first :
the effect of freeing wood of all duties and the resultant mass of
Customs formalities was to permit a far larger number of persons
to enter the business, not only at the ports, but also inland.
Formerly the large importers had retained the softwood import
trade almost in their own hands.   The provision of large sums
of cash to pay the duties, the understanding of their complica-
tions, and the obligations to pass the entries before the smallest
delivery could be effected had prevented small buyers from
operating at the import level.   Now all this was changed.
Abroad an immediate expansion of production took place in
all the Baltic countries, principally in Sweden and Norway.
Between 1850 and 1875 the value of timber exported from
Sweden increased no less than five times.   In 1860 the productions of the best Swedish mills could be had round about £10
per standard f.o.b. (free on board).   In 1870, owing to the
Franco-Prussian War, the price stood higher, at £15 per standard.
The boom in trade brought about by this war—at one time the
Bank Rate stood at 9 per cent.—was followed in 1875 by a
disastrous slump.   There were many bankruptcies in all trades,
including the timber trade.   Messrs R. W. Anderson of Carlisle
report a contract entered into by them in 1879 for 100 standards
Swedish Whitewood at less than £5 per standard c.i.f. (cost,
insurance, freight) the Tyne.   By 1873 Canada had lost to Sweden
the first place among softwood exporters to this country.   It
took seventy years for the wheel of destiny to come full circle,
and it was 1941 before Canada once more headed the list.   Sweden
in her turn was later to give place to Russia.   In 1872 the total
imports of timber into Great Britain amounted to five million
loads, with a value of approximately £13½ m. sterling.   Considering the size of the trade and the many influences at work,

the price of good Swedish Red Deals remained remarkably constant between 1870 and 1914, as will be shown by the following quotations :

1870. £10 per standard f.o.b.
1874. £15   ,,   ,,
1880. £11   ,,   ,,
1890. £12 10s.   ,,   ,,
1895. £11 10s.   ,,   ,,
1900. (Boer War) £16 10s. per standard f.o.b.
1910. £17 per standard f.o.b.
1913. £16 10s.   ,,   ,,

By 1870 Russian softwoods both from the White Sea and St Petersburg were beginning to make their presence felt in large quantities, although it was some years before Sweden lost pride of place. The actual date was 1875, when total Russian imports amounted to £2,245,880, with Sweden at £2,205,875. The price of 3rd Archangel Red Deals in 1880 was £6 per standard f.o.b., and thence onward the Russian prices were consistently £5 to £6 below their Swedish rivals, instanced by the fact that in 1913 the Russian price was £10 per standard. Up to the middle of the nineteenth century most of London's timber trade was done from large timber wharves standing on the south bank of the Thames in the Lambeth district. It has been stated that in those days more than half the working population of those parts was employed in the timber trade. With the development of the Surrey Commercial Docks, however, many merchants found it convenient to deal from City offices and to store their wood in the docks. Periodic auctions were held at the Baltic, Threadneedle Street, and other public rooms.

In those days the St Petersburg Standard had not yet become generally adopted. Memel Deals were sold at per 120 twelve feet of 3″ × 11″ ; Danzig Deals at per 40 ft. of 3″ ; Quebec Spruce per 120 twelve feet of 3″ × 9″, but ends from the same sources were sold 120 six feet of 3″ × 9″. To show the general confusion, as many as three different standards of measurement could be found on bills of lading from Christiania. The St Petersburg or Leningrad Standard, which originally consisted of 120 pieces of 12′ × 11″ × 1½″ or their equivalent, amounting to a measurement unit of 165 ft. cube, or 1980 feet super, has now gained general adoption, and is used by all countries having commerce in softwoods. All this softwood timber from the Baltic was conveyed to London and other ports by Swedish and Finnish four- and six-masted sailing-ships.

At this time the timber trade was sharply differentiated into its separate spheres of activity. The agents had their regular shippers, and sold only to the importers, while each importer had his intimate list of country merchants whom he supplied. Life in the outports was a very tranquil affair, summer being largely devoted to receiving and storing cargoes, while the winter was the time allocated for selling and distribution. We are told of the annual arrival of the Quebec Fleet laden with yellow pine-logs at Cardiff. The logs would be stored by importers at the East Dock, and the country merchants would be advised to come down and mark their logs. Each customer would have his own pitsawyers, and would stay in Cardiff maybe a month, super-intending the sawing and dispatch of his logs. In those days importers' representatives travelled into the countryside either on horseback or in traps. Income-tax was 3*d*. in the pound, and nationalization unknown. By the eighties, however, the substitution of steamers for sailing-ships introduced a quicker tempo into the timber trade. The foundations of the modern teak trade were laid during the nineteenth century. The principal supplies were obtained from India, Burma, Java, and later Siam. The first exports of the wood from Burma were in the form of squares marked with the famous crown and star grade-marks, according to their quality. Later large sawmills were installed in Burma and Siam to produce sawn lumber. The trade from Java was in small hewn flitches. Up to the middle of the nineteenth century the large supplies of imported oak brought into Great Britain principally for shipbuilding purposes had been obtained from Danzig, Memel, Riga, and other ports of the Baltic. After the middle of the century, however, two exporting sources rapidly came to the fore, in the shape of other Central Europe and the United States of America. The great oak forests of the southern portions of the Austrian Empire (now belonging to Jugoslavia) were exploited largely by British capital and initiative. In the early days this famous oak was imported in the form of solid " Crown Wainscots " hewn into shape in the woods. Later large sawmills were erected to produce sawn

AN EIGHTEENTH-CENTURY ENGRAVING SHOWING THE BALTIC EXCHANGE
IN THREADNEEDLE STREET

Reproduced by kind permission of the Baltic Exchange.

timber. The first water-driven sawmill was erected in 1712 at
Gorsky-Kotor, in the province of Croatia, and this mill was
converted to steam-power in the year 1830.

Pioneers in the oak trade were the firms of Messrs Mallinson,
Oliver, Priday, and James Latham, all well known to present-day
buyers. It is said that the first American Oak lumber reached
London in the year 1861. The wood was originally shipped to
this country from Virginia, and there was obtained the famous
white oak known as " Virginia Oak." Later other large areas
of oak were developed in the Central and Southern States of the
U.S.A., while at the same time the red variety was brought into
use. By 1880 lumber shipments of many hardwoods from the
U.S.A. were arriving in considerable quantities. One well-
known merchant is said to have advertised his new imports by
means of a brass band playing in a wagonette with placards on
the sides : " Buy my American prime cuts." Whatever the
manner of its introduction, American sawn and graded lumber
rapidly swept the market at the expense of the log trade.

Prices were extremely cheap, as will be seen from the following quotations from Messrs James Latham's catalogue dated 1895 :
" Mahogany planks from 6d. ft. super ; Walnut from 5d. ft. ;
Oak from 4d. ft. ; Ash 6d. ft. ; Satin Walnut $4\frac{1}{2}d$. ft. ; American
Whitewood 1 in. planed full thickness $2\frac{1}{2}d$. ft. super." Meanwhile a considerable trade with Eastern Canada both in sawn
maple and birch was being steadily developed. These were the
days before the invention of plywood, and thousands of standards
of Quebec Pine Deals were imported and converted every year
into $\frac{1}{8}''$ and $\frac{1}{4}''$ for drawer-sides, wardrobe-backs, and similar
purposes. Enormous stacks of these deals ranging from 12 ft.
to 16 ft. long, $3'' \times 11''$, were piled to heights of over fifty feet.
These stacks were run up by skilled timber porters, using run-
ways consisting of the deals themselves, never more than 11"
wide. It needed a steady head ! When the stacks were broken
down it was quite an art to drop the plank endways to the
ground in such a manner that it should not be damaged. It
was quite usual for a firm to carry a stock of 100,000 of
these Quebec Pine planks. Prices ranged from 10d. per ft. run
for the first quality to as low as 3d. per ft. run for the fourth
quality. Sawing was done at the rate of $2\frac{1}{2}d$. per cut. Firms
with old records of this pine trade are Messrs Bambergers and

James Latham of London and Messrs Robert Cox, Watson, Todd of Liverpool.

Quebec Birch was shipped to this country in considerable quantities at this time, in the form of octagonal logs ranging up to 20″ wide, which were sawn into various sizes for the great coach trade of those days. $\frac{1}{2}$″ Birch, 18″ to 20″ wide, was sold for 5d. per ft. super, with 1″ at 7d. Together with these logs came a great quantity of sawn birch plank shipped not only from Quebec, but also from Halifax and St John. The Quebec Birch always commanded the best price, while the latter variety was sold as low as 2s. per ft. cube to the upholstery trade. In Liverpool towards the close of the century was developed the famous trade in African Mahogany, which now supplies by far the greatest proportion of all mahogany coming to the British markets. To show the rapid growth of this new source of supply, the following import figures are interesting : 1894, 9 m. board feet ; 1897, 13 m. bd. ft. ; 1900, 18 m. bd. ft. The pioneer exporting firms operating from the West Coast of Africa were the Niger Company, the African and Eastern Trading Company, and Messrs McIver. These are all now incorporated in the United Africa Company, Ltd.

In view of the enormous consumption of plywood by almost all industries to-day, it will no doubt be difficult for readers to realize that fifty years ago the manufacture of plywood was quite in its infancy. During the eighteenth century the principle of gluing wood together in order to gain strength, using transverse grain for this purpose, was well known to cabinet-makers. In the early days veneer was flat cut, first by hand and later by power-driven saws. It was the invention of the rotary knife-cutter, towards the close of the nineteenth century, that made large sheets of veneer possible, and thus laid the secure foundations of the great plywood industry. The tea trade was one of the first trades to appreciate the commercial possibilities of the new material, and its first large use was in the manufacture of tea-chests. The experience gained in manufacturing these was put to good use, and commercial three-ply boards of many types followed quickly. The first factory for the manufacture of plywood was opened by Christian Luther at Reval, in Esthonia, in 1896. Factories were shortly afterwards established in Riga, notably by Julius Potempa, while two large factories were started at Memel. Finland and Russia were also early comers to the new industry. In fact, it was in the countries situate round the Baltic that the infant plywood industry was nurtured, no doubt due to the fact that in the vast birch forests an ideal wood was found ready to hand. Importers in the United Kingdom were not slow to appreciate the importance of the new material, which was in turn readily adopted by the consuming industries.

The nineteenth century covered a period of great development in the sawmilling industry. The modern band-mill equipped with blades up to 12″ wide was perfected towards the end of the period, thus permitting the wholesale production of sawn lumber, as was exemplified in the U.S.A. Planing machines were much improved, and their rate of feed increased. The introduction of cylindrical cutter-heads enabled moulding machines to be worked safely at a much greater speed. A word must be said here about the birth of scientifically controlled timber-seasoning. The first primitive kilns were installed both here and in the U.S.A. about 1890. The operator of those days had a choice of either baking his wood or smoke-curing it, the original kilns being based on the systems of either heating the chambers in which the wood was placed or circulating smoke through the stacks.

A special object of interest to the hardwood trade at the beginning of the twentieth century was the introduction of what was in fact the last of the commercial oaks to reach the market. Japanese Oak first came to the United Kingdom in the year 1905 in the shape of shipments of logs. The early parcels were largely shipped through the agency of Messrs Mitsui, and the logs were quickly followed by shipments of well-produced lumber. Messrs W. W. Howard Bros., of Canning Town, London, were pioneers in this trade. By 1920 a large number of Japanese producers had entered the market, and shipments to Europe reached the respectable total of two million ft. cube per annum. The timber came principally from the Northern Island of Hokkaido, and was largely shipped from the port of Otaru.

From 1905 to 1914 the timber trade pursued an even way. Prices did not move much, as is exemplified by the fact that in June 1914 the price of Swedish third-quality Red Deal was in the neighbourhood of £13 to £14 per standard. The outbreak of the war in August 1914 found the Government with no plans

to control the timber trade, or, indeed, any other trade. In the
first year or two of the War prices rose very steeply. Shortly
after the outbreak of the War a Government Timber Buyer in
the person of Mr Montague Meyer was appointed, and he bought
for all Government Departments. By 1917 prices had risen to
such high levels that it was found necessary to appoint a Government Controller in the person of Mr James Ball (later Sir James),
and maximum selling prices were fixed. To give some idea of
prices, Swedish third-quality Deal in 1916 had risen to £28 per
standard, and by 1918 stood at £54. It will be seen that, given
comparative values, this was a rise at least equal to anything that
happened as a result of the Second World War. On the conclusion of war large Government stocks, particularly of softwoods, were liquidated by means of a trading Corporation comprising the greater number of importers. For a time all went
well, but by 1921 a general trade slump set in, and it was necessary
for the Treasury to come to the aid of the Corporation by granting substantial rebates on the agreed prices. Business-men have
long memories, and it was the remembrance of this post-war
slump that coloured the attitude of some timber importers to
the question of decontrol when it was first discussed in 1945.
Fortunately, the immediate post-war slump of 1921 was of comparatively short duration, and the timber trade experienced a
decade of prosperous trading until 1930, when the ' great slump '
set in in no uncertain fashion. Prices of softwoods remained
comparatively stable during the twenties. One of the recurring
problems of the softwood trade during this period was the
handling of the continually increasing offerings of timber from
the U.S.S.R. State trading organizations were set up in London,
and handled all the U.S.S.R. shipments whether from Leningrad,
Archangel, or the Kara Sea. More than one group of importers
was formed in order to deal with these large imports on a reasonable trading basis. Canadian exports of softwoods to the United
Kingdom fell back somewhat immediately after the First World
War, and it was not until the thirties that Canada greatly increased her shipments to this country ; since then she has played
a predominant part in furnishing our softwood supplies.

The hardwood trade remained on a profitable basis during
this decade. An interesting feature was the marked interest taken
in the new range of decorative and secondary timbers from the

British Empire. Much interest was created in these timbers at the time of the British Empire Exhibition at Wembley in 1924 and 1925. At the Exhibition a number of Dominions and Colonies, such as Australia, India, Nigeria, Ghana and Malaya, set up well-arranged pavilions in which to exhibit their choice woods. There were introduced on to the market for the first time on a large scale such woods as Silver Greywood, Laurel, and Haldu from India ; Obeche, Agba, and Opepe from Nigeria ; Wawa from Ghana ; Walnut, Blackbean, and Myrtle from Australia ; and Meranti from Malaya. These are but a few of the names typical of a large assortment of tropical woods, all produced in the territories of the British Commonwealth, that was submitted to consumers such as shipbuilders and the furniture trade. Prominent firms marketing these timbers suitable for both decorative and constructional purposes were Messrs Ashton of Manchester and Messrs W. W. Howard Bros., Messrs James Latham, Ltd, and Messrs William Mallinson and Sons, Ltd, of London. By and large, however, the hardwood market was dominated by the lumber shipments from the U.S.A., Japan, and the Philippines. This lumber was splendidly produced, and sold at comparatively cheap prices, while contract terms and shipment could be relied upon by the buyers. Great Britain depended upon West Africa for the largest proportion of her mahogany, shipments being received from the British, French, and Belgian Colonial possessions. Considerable shipments of logs also continued to arrive from Honduras, Nicaragua, Mexico, and Cuba. These supplies were handled by the periodical auction sales conducted in London by the agent houses of Messrs Churchill and Sim, Ltd, Foy, Morgan, and Co., Ltd, C. Leary and Co., and in Liverpool by Messrs Edward Chaloner and Co. (Timber), Ltd, and Alfred Dobell and Co., Ltd.

The period 1920 to 1939 was a time of considerable building activity, and many fine buildings were erected, particularly in the Metropolis. Architects vied with one another in using fine wood in the lavish designs of their interior decoration, exotic hardwoods, mahogany, walnut, and oak and veneered panelling being used to an unprecedented extent. Fortunately most of these buildings survived the blitz. Noteworthy examples in London are the new Bank of England, Lloyd's, India House, South Africa House, the Imperial Chemical buildings on

Millbank, and Unilever House. Since the Second World War there have been only two opportunities to match these fine buildings, first symbolically enough in the reconstructed House of Commons. Here the superb English Oak assembled for the panelling and joinery will, we hope, do credit to the timber trade for many centuries to come. Secondly, the new Royal Festival Hall, with its beautiful veneered panels of elm, walnut, and teak, all constructed to reproduce faithfully the tones of the great orchestras that play in that celebrated hall. While planning the building the architect, Dr Martin, and his advisers toured the most famous concert-halls in the world before deciding that a wooden interior was their only answer to the problem of true reproduction of musical sound.

It is not for us here to attempt to elucidate the causes of the ' great slump.' Many thousands of words have been written on this subject, and probably the exact reasons for this trading calamity are not yet truly known. In September 1931 the British Government declared its intention to abandon the Gold Standard. On this occasion the operation was successful, and undoubtedly shielded the United Kingdom from the worst results of the world panic. At this time, as with other commodities, sellers were glutted with timber for which there were no buyers. Devaluation did undoubtedly greatly assist Great Britain's export trade, while its effect on the cost of her imports, at any rate as far as timber was concerned, was not adverse, as will be seen from the fact that in 1930 the average price of Swedish 7″ Unsorted Redwood Battens was £13 10s. per standard ; in 1931, £11 10s. ; 1932, £10 10s. ; and 1933, £9 15s. In 1931 the British Government announced its intention of levying a 10-per-cent. Customs duty on all imports. Arising out of this decision, the Ottawa Conference was convened and the system of Imperial Preference established. The Timber Trade Federation of the United Kingdom sent a delegation under Major Archibald Harris (now Sir Archibald) to place the views of the timber trade before the Conference. Traders will recollect that during the middle thirties Canada exported large quantities of Douglas Fir and Hemlock to this country in excellent specifications and at low prices, £15 per standard c.i.f. London being a typical figure for merchantable grades. It is a matter of interest that these Canadian softwoods were employed in many housing estates erected during the five years preceding the Second World War, particularly in the County of London and the South of England. Meanwhile, soft-wood imports from the European countries were well main-tained. During this period, in fact, there were larger offerings than the import trade of this country could conveniently absorb. Sweden, Finland, Russia, Poland, Jugoslavia, and Roumania all contributed their quotas. At this time the trade were negotiating with the Russians through a body known as Timber Distributors, Ltd, in which all the leading importers had an interest. In view of the present level of timber exports from the U.S.S.R., it is interesting to note that for the year 1935 the Russians requested that their quota of imports should be no less than 500,000 standards.

During the year 1934, out of a total import of 37 million cubic feet of hardwoods, no less than one-third was oak. The bulk of it went into the manufacture of oak furniture, which was then very popular with the public. About 8 million cubic feet of this oak came from the U.S.A., and the balance from Japan, Poland, and Jugoslavia. Importers watched with great interest the effects of President Roosevelt's New Deal. A series of regulations, known generally as the Lumber Code, pegged wages and prices, and instituted fair working conditions in the American industry. The effect of all this was to produce higher prices for the resultant product. The import of Empire hardwoods, par-ticularly lumber, was considerably handicapped by the lack of a consistent set of grading rules. In 1935 a Committee was set up at the Imperial Institute which produced a series of Empire Timber Grading Rules for the use of producers.

The decade 1930 to 1940 was a period of both expansion and consolidation in the plywood trade. The ' great slump ' left as its aftermath a period of difficult trading. Importers were faced with a glut of supplies from all sources. This was accompanied by falling prices and an indifferent trade organization which made it difficult for importers to deal with the shippers. By 1936, however, these difficulties had been largely mastered, the ply-wood trade had become well organized, and a period of profit-able trading commenced. One of the features of this time was a greatly increased production of plywood from the U.S.S.R. Not only did quantities increase, but also the production of higher-quality grades was successfully undertaken. Of the years

1937 to 1939 it is sufficient to say that the timber trade in all its branches came under the influence of the rearmament programme. This was a period of firm markets, increased turnover, and profitable trading. And so we come to the fateful summer of 1939. Prices had risen somewhat, but trade was good. Wood was coming forward in plentiful supplies and of a quality that has not been seen since. Timber importers and consumers will recall with longing the Swedish Red of the best productions, the Archangel Yellow and White, the Kara Sea shipments, and the excellent planed goods and floorings. In the hardwood trade the endless cars of faultlessly graded American and Japanese Oak lumber, the shiploads of prime teak, the consignments of mahogany logs, and the parcels of Slavonian Wainscot Oak will spring to the memory. And the low prices !

Unlike 1914, the declaration of war on Sunday September 3, 1939, found the Government with plans fully prepared to take over control of industry. Under the Ministry of Supply a Timber Control Department, planned and organized in advance, with Major Archibald Harris (now Sir Archibald) as Controller, sprang into action almost overnight. The Head Offices were located in Bristol, and four Deputy Controllers in the persons of Sir William Mallinson, Mr Gerald Lenanton (later Sir Gerald), Mr Powell, and Mr Edward Monkhouse (now Sir Edward) took charge of the various departments. An elaborate organization was set up to deal with such matters as the purchasing and importation of timber, shipping, consumption and licensing, and finance. The country was divided into a number of areas for convenience of administration, and Area Offices with Area Officers in charge were established, the principal offices being in London, Liverpool, and Glasgow. The Timber Control was generally regarded as one of the more successful raw-material controls established by the Government. An Advisory Committee composed of members representing all branches of the trade and all areas of the country was appointed and met regularly to discuss the current problems with the Controller and his officials. For a few months importers and merchants were left some freedom of disposal of their own stocks, although the control immediately took over all buying and forward contracts, but soon an elaborate system of quota holders and wharfingers was set up. The occupation of Norway and the control of the

Baltic by the Germans in the spring of 1940, together with the collapse of France a few months later, introduced a new urgency into the Timber Controller's task.   With supplies from the Baltic completely eliminated, recourse was made, as in the Napoleonic Wars, to the softwoods of the New World.   Canada and the U.S.A. responded nobly.   It has been truly said that without Canadian supplies the industries of the United Kingdom which depend upon timber for their raw material could not have been kept in being during the crucial years 1941 to 1944.   Canada's maximum export to the United Kingdom was reached in the year 1940, when no less a figure than 718,002 standards were imported into this country.   For hardwoods, besides supplies of the dollar countries, a great increase in production from the West African Colonial territories took place.   Not only British Colonies, but also those of Belgium and Free France, played their part.   The enemy naturally made all the difficulties they possibly could, and as the submarine warfare rose the consumption of timber had to be cut down and down.   In spite of the utmost economy, however, timbermen were comforted by the fact that it was obvious that wood was an essential raw material —in fact, it was well said that it was not until timber became in short supply that consumers realized its real value.   In addition to the perils of the sea, the fire-raising of the Luftwaffe induced a wholesale evacuation of wood from the ports and cities to the countryside.   This especially affected London, Liverpool, and the north-eastern ports.   In particular, an elaborate system of dispersal wharves operated by the trade was set up in the Home Counties from which the large wood-consuming industries of the Metropolis were supplied.   It is proper here to refer to the immense efforts put forward in the production of home-grown timber during the vital war years.   When the full extent of the emergency became clear the Government transferred the direct responsibility for the production of home-grown timber from the Timber Control and the Forestry Commission to a newly established Home-grown Timber Production Department operating within the Ministry of Supply.   Sir James Calder became the first Director in February 1941.   In July of the same year Sir James Calder was appointed Adviser on Timber Production to the Ministry of Supply, and he was succeeded as Director by Mr Gerald Lenanton (later Sir Gerald), with Mr A. Colin C.

Darby as Deputy Director. The operations of the Timber Control, the Forestry Commission, and the Home-grown Timber Production Department were co-ordinated by a Timber Control Board under the Chairmanship of Mr George Dallas, the former Chairman of the T.U.C.

A Consultative Committee of timber merchants interested in the production of home-grown timber and represented by the Federated Home-grown Timber Merchants' Association and the Timber Trade Federation of the United Kingdom was established and met representatives of the Timber Control Board monthly. Similar arrangements were made for Scotland with the co-operation of the Scottish Home-grown Association. This reorganization at the top, combined with the appointment of Regional Production Officers (aimed at securing the co-operation of the trade, which was readily given), soon bore fruit. The production of home-grown timber, which for the years 1934 to 1938 averaged 75,000 standards of softwood and 10 million cubic feet of hardwood, rose to its highest figure in the year 1942 with 297,800 standards of softwood and 50,800,000 cubic feet of hardwood. This great increase in production was achieved in three ways : (i) in old-established home-grown mills ; (ii) by the fact that many importers turned over their sawmills in ports and cities to the conversion of home-grown timber ; (iii) by the installation of temporary mills in the woods. In addition, the Home-grown Timber Production Department operated a number of temporary Government mills. These were worked by skilled lumbermen from Canada, Australia, New Zealand, Newfoundland, British Honduras, and last, but by no means least, by members of the Women's Timber Corps.

CHAPTER V

POST-WAR RECONSTRUCTION AND AFTER

WHEN it became obvious that the fall of Germany would not be long delayed a special Decontrol Committee of the Timber Trade Federation of the United Kingdom under its President, Mr J. L. Baynes, C.B.E., of Messrs Gabriel, Wade, and English, Ltd, held many consultations with the Timber Controller, Sir Archibald Harris, and members of the Timber Control to determine how the timber trade could best be returned to private enterprise. Sectional Decontrol Committees were set up covering the various branches of the trade and held frequent meetings. As a result, the Softwood Importers were the first branch to obtain at least partial decontrol. In 1946 the National Softwood Brokers, Ltd, was established. This was a Corporation staffed by members of the agency firms whose duty it was to distribute the softwood purchases made by Timber Control on a quota basis to the importers, the wood being sold c.i.f.—that is to say, delivered in the United Kingdom at the port of importation. But meanwhile consumption licensing of softwood, hardwood, and plywood was maintained, together with price control. In the event, the Government treated the three great branches of the timber trade differently as far as the manner of decontrol was concerned. As the method and timing of decontrol largely influenced the trading of each branch in immediate post-war years, it will be clearer from the reader's point of view to review softwoods, hardwoods, and plywood separately in the decade following the Second World War to the present day. .

In 1947 Sir Archibald Harris retired from the post of Timber Controller, after eight years of devoted, arduous work. He was succeeded by Mr Edward Monkhouse, C.B.E. (now Sir Edward), who had been a Deputy Controller for many years. Sir Edward Monkhouse's Deputy Controllers were Mr R. Latham, C.B.E., Mr Gordon Clark, and Mr T. L. Lees.

During the period of operation of the National Softwood Brokers, Ltd, approximately five years, the Government target for the importation of softwoods was set at roughly 1 million standards, although the immediate pre-war figure had been nearly double. This fact caused a lot of complaint among members of the trade, and representations on the matter were continually made to the Ministry of Materials. Early in 1951 softwood importers were granted freedom to import on their own account wood from the Baltic, and a number of other countries outside the Iron Curtain, including the U.S.A. and Canada, although the trade was still restricted by a global quota of about a million and a quarter standards. At the same time the Board of Trade freed softwoods from price control, although consumer licensing was still maintained. The National Softwood Brokers, Ltd, was shortly afterwards wound up, after what was generally considered to be an effectual career under its Chairman, Mr Frank Urmston, a well-known agent with wide experience and worldwide knowledge of the timber trade.

By 1953 the Board of Trade were still licensing for consumption only some 1,100,000 standards per annum. The softwood trade continued its pressure on the Government to remove consumer licensing, and on November 13, 1953, the Ministry of Materials gave notice abolishing consumer licensing. At last the softwood trade was free ! At the end of 1953 the United Kingdom's stock of softwood stood at 748,500 standards ; 1954, 495,700 standards, with 1,689,374 standards at December 1955. Following complete decontrol, importers purchased about 1,350,000 standards for delivery to the United Kingdom in 1954, and this import figure reached 1,500,000 standards in the succeeding years. The composition and total quantity of softwoods imported in the years 1938 and 1955 respectively are interesting ; only the principal exporting countries are shown individually. Here are the figures in standards :

	1938	1955
Canada	403,586	431,745
Finland	406,720	321,042
Poland	117,582	52,256
Sweden	339,318	456,160
U.S.A.	36,007	13,887
U.S.S.R. (including Baltic States)	451,755	241,209
Others	38,379	173,075
	1,793,347	1,689,374

It is to be observed that the contribution of the U.S.S.R. including the Baltic States has fallen by nearly half from 451,755 to 241,209 standards. Finland also shows a drop of some 85,000 standards, while Sweden has advanced her contribution by 117,000 standards, from 339,318 to 456,160 standards.

The hardwood trade had to wait longer for its freedom. In October 1946, however, an interesting order, the Hardwood Overseas Procurement Order, Part III (H.O.P. III for short), was issued by the Ministry of Materials. This reserved for Government importation only some score of the principal commercial hardwoods, including dollar woods, and threw the rest of the import open to private enterprise. Importers literally rushed into action and scoured the earth for usable timber. Forest areas were tapped which had never before contributed exports to the United Kingdom. Such woods as Rauli, Laurel, and Coigue from Chile ; Freijo, Jequitiba, and Louro Vermelho from Brazil ; and Katon from Siam were imported in considerable quantities and eagerly bought by timber-hungry consumers. The use of these new timbers was greatly helped by the scientific research and investigations carried out by the Forest Products Research Laboratory, Princes Risborough, Bucks, and the Timber Development Association. At one time over 350 different species of hardwoods figured in the Customs Entry forms. The results must have surprised even the Ministry of Materials. In the spring of 1949 hardwood, with the exception of dollar woods, was freed from consumption licence. On January 16, 1950, the hardwood trade was practically returned to private enterprise, inasmuch as complete freedom of import was permitted to private traders, with the exception of dollar woods, while maximum prices were abolished. It was not, however, until 1955 that a restricted quota of £3,000,000 was granted to the hardwood trade for the import of wood from Canada and the U.S.A. Since 1950 the import of hardwoods into the United Kingdom has remained steady at about 40 million cubic feet per annum. A feature of the hardwood trade since the Second World War has been the great increase in the production of tropical wood, both in the form of lumber and logs from territories within the British Commonwealth. A number of sawmills have been established in Ghana, Nigeria, Malaya, Borneo, and Sarawak. Such woods as Wawa, Obeche, Meranti,

Keruen, and Ramin have been imported into the United
Kingdom in large quantities, and proved themselves well able
to stand up to renewed competition by lumber from traditional
sources of supply, like the U.S.A. In 1938 the total importation
of hardwoods of all descriptions into the United Kingdom was
approximately 38,000,000 ft. cube, of which only 4,000,000 ft.
cube was in the shape of logs, the remainder being sawn lumber.
During the Second World War and the years following the
proportion of logs to sawn lumber became much higher, as
much as half the total import. This caused a considerable boom
in the home sawmilling trade, resulting as it did largely from the
cessation of American lumber shipments. By 1956 the proportion of logs had fallen back to some 25 per cent., mainly owing
to the production of lumber by the tropical sawmills located in
the British Commonwealth.

Here is a comparative analysis of the countries of origin of
hardwood imports given in cubic feet for the years 1938 and
1955 ; logs and sawn timber are combined.

	1938	1955
Australia	1,390,680	327,760
Borneo (North)	889,223	798,875
Burma	1,763,863	632,709
Canada	6,976,613	2,218,203
Finland	1,509,743	583,288
France.	157,370	3,621,049
French Africa . . .	491,203	1,943,194
Ghana	507,605	6,695,124
Japan	1,013,637	3,229,377
Jugoslavia	2,770,414	3,130,105
Nigeria	1,206,729	9,491,252
Philippines	633;307	1,265
Poland	2,715,984	43,099
Siam (Thailand) . . .	476,702	1,059,711
U.S.A.	13,139,958	1,341,654
Others	3,020,596	10,143,921
	38,663,627	45,260,586

The changed picture of post-war hardwood imports is very
noticeable. It will be seen that Australia has reduced her export

to the United Kingdom by approximately 1 million ft. cube, due largely to her own rising internal consumption of wood. The Burmese export, mainly teak, has fallen by over a million ft. cube, but, on the other hand, Siam (Thailand) has put on more than $\frac{1}{2}$ million ft. cube. This, being mostly teak, has done something to redress the balance of this timber, so necessary for shipbuilding and other industries. The imports into the United Kingdom from both Canada and the U.S.A. have fallen very considerably indeed as compared with pre-war days, and this was due to the Treasury restrictions on the use of dollars. The gap in imports from Canada and the U.S.A. has been filled by tropical hardwoods from French Equatorial Africa, Ghana, and Nigeria. It will be seen that these areas have very substantially increased their exports to Great Britain. Japan's export of oak has risen by over 2 million ft. cube, and has largely replaced the traditional American Oak used for so long in this country.

The plywood trade was firmly controlled by the Government, and it was not until 1953 that the Ministry of Materials at last decided to quit its large stocks of all dimensions and descriptions. A scheme was then operated by which the trader was permitted to import from abroad on his own account one unit for every two units purchased from National Stock. Later, as National Stock fell, the scheme was altered to a balance of unit for unit. By the end of 1954 the Government balances were largely cleared, and the plywood trade was given freedom to import on open general licence with the exception of goods from Canada and the United States. Later this licence was extended to cover the import of softwood plywoods from dollar sources. The plywood trade speedily returned to its traditional sources of supply, and large importations took place from Finland, the U.S.S.R., Sweden, and Germany. In addition, production of plywood made from tropical woods such as Gaboon, Sapele, Mahogany, Obeche, and similar timbers was received from factories established since the Second World War in territories such as Nigeria, French Equatorial Africa, and the Belgian Congo. Prominent among these successful enterprises is the African Timber and Plywood Company's factory at Sapele. This Company is a subsidiary of Messrs Lever Brothers. Nevertheless, the plywood trade importation in 1955 amounted to 15,134,164

cubic feet, as compared with 10,861,755 cubic feet in the year
1938. Here is an analysis of the figures into principal countries
of origin for the two years, given in cubic feet :

	1938	1955
Finland	4,819,599	7,077,392
Germany	199,242	669,874 (West)
Japan	382,664	1,461,768
Poland	556,098	105,977
Sweden	217,563	151,130
U.S.A.	278,155	3,690
U.S.S.R. (including Baltic States)	3,556,022	2,569,931
Others	852,412	3,094,402
	10,861,755	15,134,164

The post-war picture of plywood imports shows the U.S.A.
contribution to be negligible, again owing to currency restrictions. The import from the U.S.S.R. and Baltic States has fallen
by 1 million ft. cube, but, on the other hand, Finland has more
than filled the gap here by raising her exports of similar types of
plywood by approximately 2 million ft. cube. The figure of
199,242 ft. cube for Germany before the War comprises the
export of the whole of pre-war Germany, while the amount of
669,874 ft. cube under 1955 is for Western Germany only, showing how much this area has increased her industrial activity.
The increase under " Others " from 852,412 to 3,094,402 ft. cube
has been largely brought about by the productions from new
plywood mills installed in tropical West Africa in the territories
of Ghana, Nigeria, and French Equatorial Africa.

It is an interesting fact that, taking the import of basic raw
materials such as wool, cotton, metal ores, rubber, and wood,
timber ranked first in order of value in 1955 with £192·8 m.,
being 17·2 per cent. of the total amount of the £1,123·8 m. bill.
Timber also occupied the first position in the year 1938, when
the percentage of the whole it represented was 17·3. During
the years of restriction and consumption licensing timber fell in
1950 to the fourth place, recovering to the second place in 1954.

We have now safely transported the reader over the long
and, it is hoped, interesting and not uneventful journey through

this fascinating timber trade from the days of Pharaoh's carpenters and the royal timber merchant Hiram, King of Tyre,
to the present day.   During these four thousand years we have
found the trade passing through many vicissitudes and changes,
some due to its own volition, but mostly brought about by the
pressure of historical change.   It is meet, therefore, before taking
another journey in order to survey the great timber-producing
areas of the world and learn their story, to take a look at the
organization of the timber trade in our country to-day.   The
structure of the trade is like that of the tree which produces its
essential raw material.   The producers are the roots from which
the whole edifice springs, the agents and importers are the trunk
through which the sap—otherwise the stream of sawn timber—
flows continually to the furthermost branches and twigs, which
exemplify the hundreds of industries which depend upon wood
in some shape or other to supply their needs.   Some industries
take their supplies in the form of softwood deals and battens,
others in the shape of hardwood boards and plank, while others
depend largely upon plywood and veneers.   The timber trade
is indeed a house with many rooms !   However, our immediate
business is to discuss the structure of the trade ;   to its numerous
and fascinating ramifications we will return later.

Timber is produced equally in countries which border upon
the equator or fringe the arctic snows.   In some places men wait
for the summer rains to flood the rivers, so that they can float
their timbers ;   in others they pray for a hard and frosty winter,
so that the trees may be hauled over the snow through territories
otherwise impassable owing to marsh and swamp.   There is
one thing in common with all these operations :   much fore-
thought is required.   Timber extraction on the scale required by
modern sawmilling is a matter for scientific planning and specialized plant.   Sometimes the sawmiller buys logs from an independent logging firm, but usually to-day the operation of
logging is part of the sawmilling enterprise, particularly if it is
an integral part of a large organization.   To indicate the scale
of modern logging enterprise, Messrs MacMillan and Bloedel,
Ltd, of British Columbia, logs for itself and its associated companies every year more than 300 million board feet of various
species.   In some undertakings the producers own their timber
concessions ;   in other cases the logs are bought by auction from

Government at periodic auctions or from privately owned forest-land by negotiation. It is interesting that in Burma teak-trees are purchased from the Forest Department three or four years before it is proposed to fell, in order that the trees may be killed by girdling right round the bark, so that the logs become light enough to float down the river to the sawmills at the port. Whatever the method, the sawmill receives its logs, which are sawn to the best advantage, and the resultant timber is graded by skilled brackers into many grades and sizes ready for export.

This is where the agent steps in and performs his valuable function. For to operate successfully the producer must sell every piece of wood that is manufactured, whatever its size, whatever its grade. Whereas there are very few importers who can handle such a variety, it is the duty of the agent, with his specialized knowledge of the market, to take his principal's stock-sheets and match them to the manifold demands of different importers, so that by the end of the season a complete clearance has been effected. Many agents have represented the same shippers, particularly in the Baltic, for years, and in some cases literally for generations—thus confidence is engendered and commerce flows easily through old-established channels. The agent works under the ægis of a contract agency, and frequently for an additional remuneration undertakes to cover the *del credere* risk. In addition he may assist the shipper to finance his production during the winter months.

The importer has a variety of functions to perform. Basically these consist of purchasing the timber in the country of origin, arranging for shipment to the United Kingdom, and finally conveying it to the consumer. But the exact way in which the individual importer carries out these duties may vary immensely. For instance, he may deal in either the softwood or hardwood branch of the trade. His business may be established in a large port, such as London, or a smaller port, of which there are many ; he may make a practice of storing wood to season for ultimate delivery to customers, or his habit may be to sell overside to merchants, who in their turn distribute.

Let us deal firstly with a softwood importer operating in a large port and selling mainly to merchants. Such an importer would have old-established connexions with shippers in the Baltic, Canada, or the United States. The productions of the same mills would be bought year after year. Usually the business would be done on a ' free on board ' (f.o.b.) basis, and the importer would arrange his own freights, using his judgment as to the shipping market. Occasionally, however, the contracts would be arranged on a c.i.f. basis (cost, insurance, freight), under which, roughly speaking, the shipper or his agent arranges the freight and the insurance and collects the cost of this service, together with the price of the wood, from the importer. Now, such an importer would negotiate every year through various agents and from different shippers for specifications of sawn and planed wood of various kinds. As he made his contracts he would be considering the special requirements of his customers. Some of these would require one dimension, and some another ; some the highest-quality timber, some carcassing wood. It would be the importer's business to make his purchases up into such varied bills of lading as would suit his customers' individual requirements. Such bills of lading would always be on c.i.f. terms. The importer would also have to space out his shipments through the season to suit both the shippers on the one hand and his customers on the other. In the Baltic there is usually a rush for first open-water goods—that is to say, lumber that is shipped as soon as the ports are free of ice. In the case of British Columbia and other softwood countries in temperate zones, such as Brazil and Jugoslavia, shipments take place evenly throughout the whole year.

Now, if, on the other hand, our softwood importer's business consisted of a well-equipped wharf, with ancillary sawmill, situated in London or a flourishing outport, he would normally proceed somewhat differently, especially if the business was mainly with consumers. The buying would be done through agents, as in the case of importer No. 1, but would be conducted with special care to suit the buyer's particular trade. If the wharf in question had a harbour frontage, as is customary in many ports, and could take ocean-going ships, then the buying would have to be closely related to shipment date, so as to avoid unnecessary congestion and resultant heavy demurrage. Such an importer would probably have both a merchant and consumer business. The merchants would take their goods from him overside, so as to save handling charges, and so in normal times would, probably, some of the big consumers. The bulk of the

UNLOADING TIMBER IN THE SURREY COMMERCIAL DOCKS
Fox Photos.

shipments, however, would be landed on the importer's wharf, sorted, tallied, and carefully stored away, the best quality of joinery deals under cover in sheds, and the remainder in the open. As our importer has a sawmill, he will be at some advantage in his buying, as he will be able to purchase at a suitable reduction a number of sizes and dimensions which are not readily saleable by the shipper as they stand. These he would re-saw to good advantage in the aforementioned sawmill, and sell at a fair price. The equipment of a wharf or yard is a matter for careful consideration if large quantities of softwood are to be handled economically, especially as the shipping season is short and congested. Some are laid out with a system of railway-lines or tram-tracks to take trucks and bogies. Others depend on a good road system on which tractors and trailers are used. The most modern equipment is that of forklift trucks, which will pile timber over 20 ft. high, and straddle wagons to transport it. But both these require exceptionally good, level roads to operate successfully. Large cranes can be used with jibs up to 100 ft. long. These give great flexibility and cover a large area. Gantries up to five tons weight and 50 ft. span are also useful adjuncts. However, owing to the seasonal nature of the softwood importing trade, sheer manpower is still, one might say, the main standby.

Now we come to the large importer who specializes mainly in hardwoods. Such a firm usually has wharves and yards of its own, and it will be more instructive for our purpose to assume that we are dealing with such a one. The business will probably be situated in London or Liverpool, because, owing to their excellent general shipping facilities, the larger hardwood yards are usually to be found in one of these ports. If in London, the situation will probably be on one of the canals or tributaries associated with the river Thames, the river Lea being much favoured by the hardwood trade in this respect ; or, if in Liverpool, the yard will be within reach of the waterfront. The hardwood importer's business is considerably more intricate than that of the softwood branch, inasmuch as the former has to deal with a far greater variety of both species and qualities. To such an extent is this true that over 350 species of hardwoods have been known to be listed in Customs Returns in one year. The large importer deals through agents, as does his softwood confrère. However, as his goods are received from literally all over the world, he has to keep in touch with a much greater number of markets. Further, he has to concern himself with many considerations arising from such items as import and export licences, currency restrictions, dollar woods, barter agreements, and so on. The great bulk of hardwood is imported on c.i.f. terms, and owing to the small nature of many of the consignments, great use is made of what are known as liner bills of lading—i.e., the parcel of timber is shipped as part of a mixed cargo.

Besides the business of being an importer, the hardwood yard-keeper has the special task of conveying the goods to his customers in a seasoned condition. This entails the provision of adequate sheds and stacking-ground. These must be equipped with good roads and/or rail-tracks, and in large wharves it is usual to provide a variety of gantry and jib cranes to facilitate the handling of consignments. It used to be said among old-fashioned timber-men that seasoning should be at the rate of one year for every inch of thickness. In other words, a 3″ oak plank should be naturally air-dried for three years to bring it into prime condition. The task of holding a seasoned stock is now facilitated by the fact that the science of kiln-drying has made rapid strides during the past few years. Many large hardwood operators now maintain batteries of kilns which enable them to supply scientifically seasoned lumber to their customers at comparatively short notice. Some of the hardwood wharves have a sawmill attached both for the conversion of logs and the preparation of lumber. This is very convenient, and saves moving the stock from place to place. The existence of a mill involves the provision of powerful gantries and other cranes capable of lifting up to ten tons in order that the cargoes of solid logs may be received and stored. It is not, however, possible in a book of this sort to give more than a brief sketch of a large hardwood importer's activities. A specialized branch of the hardwood trade is that of staves, which are imported in a great variety of sizes, principally in oak, for the barrel and cooperage trade.

Plywood is a branch of the timber trade quite on its own. The plywood agent performs his duties much the same as his brethren in the softwood and hardwood trades. But the importer is faced with a fundamentally different proposition, because he is handling what is in effect a manufactured article. Plywood must be stored under cover in sheds, and kept covered as far as possible during transit. This is true in spite of modern water-proof glues, because boards left exposed to the weather soon discolour and lose their looks. Therefore the plywood importer has extensive private storage sheds, or, if not, uses the under-cover facilities provided by public docks and warehouses. Plywood arrives in this country packed in crates which are frequently bulky to handle. Consequently the provision of suitable lifting tackle is essential if the consignments are to be handled swiftly and economically. Overhead gantries, mobile cranes, self-propelled lifting trucks, all find a use for this purpose.

We now come to the decorative veneer trade. This deals with veneers specially cut to bring out the beautiful variations of grain found in a number of hardwoods, such as oak, mahogany, walnut, maple, and various tropical woods. Veneer imports reach the United Kingdom from practically all over the world. Where the imports of any one species, such as oak from Jugoslavia and France, reach large proportions, the trade is usually handled by agents selling for the producers. But the truly decorative veneers are frequently cut in small, highly specialized plants from which the British importer, who must be a man of mature judgment and skill, makes his own selection and arranges his own terms. Paris has always been a considerable centre both for cutting and marketing exotic veneers. However, a large, well-organized veneer-cutting industry has grown up in Great Britain in recent years. These plants convert the veneers required for manufacturing plywood from solid logs imported from overseas, also decorative veneers from highly figured logs which have been specially selected for the purpose, and finally a large number of home-grown oak logs for making up into veneered panels. Wallboards are another highly specialized branch of the timber trade, and, of course, a very modern addition. Originally they were a by-product of the sawmilling industry, but lately the production has grown so large that the supply of waste wood products has to be supplemented very considerably with pulp logs and other materials. One insulation board is made from the residue of sugar-cane fibres. The different origins of these various types of wallboards has led to a varied trade organization in this country. Some boards are sold by concessionnaires of the foreign companies to distributors and merchants. Others are sold through agents to importers ; others are handled by importers. There is also a considerable wallboard manufacturing industry in the United Kingdom, the products of which are mainly handled by merchant stockists.

In conclusion, a reference must be made to the home-grown trade, which, as its familiar title suggests, deals with timber grown in this country. This trade is unfortunately faced with a difficult situation at the moment owing to the patriotic efforts that were made to expand home-grown timber production during the War to meet the nation's urgent timber requirements. When it is pointed out that home-grown production rose from approximately 22 million ft. cube in 1938 to roughly 100 million ft. cube at the end of the Second World War the nature of this endeavour will be fully realized. Unfortunately it involved the felling of larger quantities of trees that normally speaking would have sustained the home-grown trade for a generation to come. The landowner frequently deals with the home-grown timber merchant direct, or on occasion use is made of country agents. There is a special class of merchants who buy standing timber from the landowner and sell the felled trees to the sawmills. In many cases such a merchant provides the services of felling and hauling. The backbone of the home-grown trade, however, is the typical home-grown merchant, with a self-contained business comprising an office, sawmills, and stacking-yards. Such a man buys his own trees, employs his own fellers, and maintains a fleet of vehicles to do his own hauling. The trees are converted in the firm's own sawmill, stacked in the yard, and later marketed through old-established connexions. Great skill, hard work, and local knowledge are needed to conduct such a business successfully over a term of years. The influence of the operations of the Forestry Commission on the home-grown trade in the years to come will continue to become increasingly evident. As the plantations which at the present moment are being planted on a large scale come to maturity it is to be hoped that once more the home-grown trade will have an adequate stock of standing timber to maintain in a healthy state an industry so essential to the national safety and economic stability.

The timber trade is well served by a number of organizations and institutions covering both the commercial and technical aspects of the business. At the head of the structure stands the Timber Trade Federation of the United Kingdom, with over

1200 members. Representatives from more than thirty sections, local associations, and affiliated bodies attend its Council Meetings, held four times a year and culminating in an Annual General Meeting whose main business is the election of a President and Vice-President. Founded in 1892, the Timber Trade Federation has numbered many illustrious timber men among its thirty-three Presidents, the first being Mr S. B. Boulton, of Messrs Burt, Boulton, and Haywood, Ltd. The office is at present graced by Mr Gordon Clark, of Messrs Churchill and Sim, Ltd, with Mr W. E. Vesey as Vice-President. The Timber Trade Federation owed its birth to an *ad hoc* body of timber importers and merchants elected from the trade in 1891 to oppose a number of Railway Rate Bills then passing through Parliament, almost its first business being to seek a meeting with the Right Hon. A. J. Mundella, M.P., President of the Board of Trade, on these matters. The founding resolution stated that its main object would be " the promotion of the common interests of the timber trade of the United Kingdom as a whole whilst preserving perfect local liberty of action to the constituent members." It may be said that the successful combining of the first and second parts of this pious resolution is still the main preoccupation of its Presidents—and the writer speaks from personal experience !

At first offices and secretarial services were provided by the London Chamber of Commerce, then installed at Botolph House, Eastcheap, E.C.3. Total expenses for the year 1894 amounted to the sum of £316 17s. 1d. The first dinner was held in 1896, and cost members £28 15s. Immediately three Committees were elected to deal with the business of the Federation—namely, the Foreign Importers' Committee, the Foreign Merchants' Committee, and the English Timber Trade Committee. Shortly afterwards an Agents' and Brokers' Committee was added to deal with agency matters. Some of the local groups now affiliated to the Timber Trade Federation were founded prior to 1892, but it may be safely said that by far the greater number of sections, associations, and institutes now covering the multitudinous activities of the timber trade owe their conception to the above four Committees. For instance, the Federated Home-grown Timber Merchants' Association to-day has a large membership among home-grown timber merchants. The National Sawmilling Association covers sawmilling matters, and the Kiln Owners'

Association deals with kilns and kiln-drying. The Federated Merchant Freighters' Association handles matters of shipping and freights. These and many another specializing Association are represented on the Timber Trade Federation Council. The Timber Trade Federation also largely finances the Timber Development Association, Ltd, which deals with timber education and public relations. Timber scientific and technical research is conducted by a Joint Committee of the Department of Scientific and Industrial Research, to which the trade contributes half the funds. The laboratories are situated at Tyler's Green, Buckinghamshire. The Institute of Wood Science (Founder President, Mr Bryan Latham) has recently been founded to provide a common meeting-ground for timber technologists, scientists, students, and others interested in promoting the scientific study of wood. The trade is well served by an energetic Timber Trades Benevolent Society, founded in 1897 at a general meeting held at the Carpenters Hall, the first President being Mr W. L. T. Foy. The present President is Mr Stanley Lloyd, the Hon. Treasurer Mr Hubert Lenanton, and the Secretary Miss M. K. Woolley.

Forestry is well covered in the United Kingdom by three strong Associations. The Empire Forestry Association, whose Patron is Her Majesty the Queen and whose Chairman is Lord Milverton, covers the Commonwealth in addition to British forestry. The Royal Forestry Society of England and Wales has as its principal object the fostering of forestry in these two countries, while the Royal Scottish Forestry Society, which has been in existence for over a hundred years, fulfils the same task for Scotland. These three organizations number members from the timber trade as well as foresters in their membership. There is a growing realization that the interests of both parties are closely interlocked. Foresters for their part have come to realize that the wood from their forests must be marketed to the best possible commercial advantage in order to ensure the stability of economy, while timber merchants feel that the scientific forester, with his urge to conserve, is no longer their enemy, as they might sometimes have thought, but, in fact, some one upon whom they depend for the regeneration of the forest and continued supply of the raw materials of their trade.

CHAPTER VI

THE BALTIC TIMBER TRADE

AT the commencement of the Christian era Poland was covered with immense forests of pine, spruce, oak, and beech. By 1300, however, settlements were eating into the primeval forests, and the need for forest laws, however crude, became apparent. Casimir the Great in 1347 published the first statutes to reduce his forest domains to some sort of order. Most of the provisions dealt with the rights of the Crown, but great care was also taken to establish the rights of all woodland owners against trespass. The third law, in Monkish Latin, read, " Si alienos porcos in tua silva reperias," which being translated means " if thou findest another man's swine in thy wood," followed by exact directions what to do ! From these vast forests the local traders procured their logs, which were floated down the Vistula and other rivers till they reached the busy ports of Danzig, Riga, and Memel, where the merchants of the Hanse received them. Coming to later days, the following extracts are taken from reports by an inspector, Mr Polytaeif, on the great forests of Volhynia in the 1850's :

> For these reasons the district of Briansk will be the principal centre of the wood enterprise. At present there are three steam and one water power sawmills ; two of them are not specially for sawing, but they can be applied to that purpose—principally they are for grinding corn. On the principle of these fabrics the sawing apparatus is for two frames each of 10 saws ; and for cutting off the edge there is a large saw. At the other mill there are 40 saws ; here they make the same sorts of timber as at the first. At the third mill there are 50 saws ; and the sawmill worked by water has 44 saws in 4 frames. The total number of logs sawn in these mills is about 50,000.

It is interesting that these early sawmills were dual purpose, inasmuch as at will they could be used for either grinding corn or sawing timber.

Here is an abridgement made from an article in an early

number of *The Timber Trades Journal* on logging as practised on the river Dnieper in the last century. The descriptions are so vivid that it richly deserves to be reproduced :

> Owners of estates and forests sell part of their wood to the wood merchants, and they know how to make the best of everything that comes into their hands. Winter begins here generally in November. In September, when the peasants have to pay their taxes, contracts are made with them, when generally those who are living together in small villages agree, and bind themselves, against an advance, to cut and drive a certain quantity of wood down to the banks of the rivers. These advances are sometimes a third or one-half of the amount they can expect to earn during the course of the winter, but when the agreement is signed by the elected members of the court of the village, or the Starosta and the Uradnisk, as they are called here, there is hardly any risk of loss. In November the peasants come to the woods, each with one or two, sometimes three, of their small pony-like horses, in the last case called " troskas," collecting together often as many as 200 to 300 horses from one village. A sort of abode for the winter is then erected in the woods, built of small poles, earth and straw, which reminds one more than anything of the huts of the Esquimaux and the Laplanders. When ready, 12 to 15 men make it their home for the winter. Furs, rags, and little boxes for provisions are placed all around, and the fire, composed of large logs, with the large saucepan, in the middle. When the work of the day is over, the workmen seat themselves each on his place round the flaming fire, on which the soup, composed of meat, cabbage and onions, boils ; this is the time to see the Russian peasant, and to hear his monotonous chant. The cutting and driving is done in this way. Every peasant has his axe ; he fells his tree, clears off all knots and branches, lays it on his sledge, and drives it to the river. Thus millions of trees are brought down these two rivers in the course of the winter. The kind of wood grown here is a sort of redwood fir, sometimes also whitewood. The fir tree grows very fast. A fir tree which requires 120 years and more to ripen in the north of Europe matures here in 80 years.

This account deals with an economy that to-day seems an age away, although really less than a hundred years !

About 1861 Mr William Quinn, Supervisor of Felling in the Crown Forests of Quebec, visited Danzig armed with letters to Her Majesty's Consul General to see what he could learn from the European trade. Mr Quinn reports as follows :

> I went with Mr Albrecht and looked over all the lumber in the river, down to the harbour. There was but little remaining after the spring shipments, and none of the new timber had then arrived. It was expected in a few days. The timber is separated into three classes—1st, 2nd, 3rd. Mr Albrecht told me that to get any considerable quantity of first quality is very difficult and expensive, and scarcely any of it is to be had without having to be hauled 30 or 40 English miles. The value of first quality redwood here at present is 55s. per load, free on board ; 2nd, 45s. ; 3rd class about 41s. per load. The freights just then were very low, not more than 15s. per load to the east coast of England. Large quantities of redwood are now being sawn up by the different establishments here into deck plank for the English and French Governments. A considerable quantity of redwood is also being prepared here, intended for the defences at Southampton, England. The pieces are all to be 35 feet long, 12 inches square, and to show a certain amount of heartwood on all sides. The price to be paid is 65s. per load, free on board—a price with which the sellers seem well satisfied.

Mr Albrecht, by the way, was a local timber merchant. Here is a list of Danzig's wood exports for the year 1860 from the Customs entries :

> The exportation of wood from Danzig in 1860 was :
>
> 229,190 pcs. of full-sized square fir timber
> 57,127 pcs. of small sized square fir timber
> 877,392 Sleepers and sleeper logs
> 326,987 Fir deck deals, deals and deal ends
> 2,066 Masts, spars, bowsprits, etc.
> 4,783 Fathoms of lathwood
> 29,346 Oak planks, 1st brack
> 29,741 Oak planks, 2nd brack
> 96,083 Unbracked oak planks and plank ends
> 36,755 pcs. of oak timber, planking logs and crooks
> 14,091 Shooks of oak staves
>
> While the prices for oak timbers per load were as follows :

	£ s. d.
Oak timber, straight, 9 to 16 in. sq., 18 ft. average length	4.15.0
Oak timber ends, 9 to 16 in. sq., 6 to 11 ft. in length	3.10.0
Oak crooks, 9 to 16 in. sq., 14 to 15 ft. average length	3. 5.0

	£ s. d.
Oak planks, 1st. brack, $2\frac{1}{2}$ in. to 7 in. thick and above ..	8. 5.0
Oak planks, 1st brack, 2 in. thick	7. 0.0
Oak planks, 2nd brack, 2 in. to 7 in. thick and above ..	5. 5.0
Oak planking logs (Plancons) hewn 27 ft. average length,	
10 to 15 inches scantling, string measure	3.15.0
Two sides sawn, string measure	4.10.0

The indefatigable Mr Quinn then proceeded to visit Memel, and reported that the port was supplied with logs from the provinces of Kovno, Augustov, Bialystok, Vitepsk, Minsk, Vilna, and Volhynia. He found, however, that the local timber trade was declining both because good logs were becoming ever scarcer and the delays in the arrival of the rafts at the port of Memel necessitated the holding over of large quantities of lumber every winter, and consequently the merchants were embarrassed from a monetary point of view. Nevertheless, he found occasion to add that the sawmillers were as busy as possible sawing and preparing timber for the French Government. It is fitting that we should make a reference here to the famous timber port of Riga. Here is the translation from an article in *Le Marchand de Bois* describing conditions in the 1870's :

> Of the ports of the Baltic provinces, Riga exports more lumber and timber than all the others, consequently a statement of the amount of the trade done at Riga will give some idea of the extent of the lumber trade of Russia in Europe. The details of the exports of Riga for a series of years . . . are taken from a recent official document issued from the bureau of commerce. The timber and lumber reaches Riga by the Dwina and its tributaries, and comes from the provinces of Livonia, Esthonia, Courland, Mohilev, and Minsk, in Lithuania. Notwithstanding the extensive devastation of the forests, carried on with no assurance of their renewal, the vast forests which formerly covered these provinces yet contain large reserves of timber of the best quality, but their continued depletion, with no provisions made for their future restoration, should give rise to serious apprehension.

It would appear that by the dawn of the twentieth century the pick of the available timber had already passed through these great Eastern Baltic ports of Danzig, Memel, and Riga. Henceforth it is a story of falling dimensions and reduced specifications to meet the necessity of converting smaller trees.

By the Middle Ages the export of timber was the mainstay of Norway's commercial economy. Norway stood in an extremely favourable position both geographically and from the point of climate. In those days of poor communications her forests came right down to the water's edge, and in the sheltered fjords timber could be loaded straight on to the little ocean-going ships and cogs. Once freighted, there was a quick sea passage across to England's east-coast ports and the Dutch harbours of Amsterdam and Rotterdam. The Gulf Stream kept the Norwegian coast comparatively free from the ice that in winter closed the Baltic ports. In those days many of the forests belonged to small landed proprietors. Almost every farmhouse had its simple sawmill, consisting often of a circular saw, fixed directly to the axle of a water-wheel. For the larger commercial operations there were plenty of rivers and waterways to float the logs to the sea. Sometimes the route was assisted by artificially constructed slides. They were about 5 ft. wide and built of trunks of young trees in the form of a chute. Extraordinary ingenuity was shown in their siting so as to take advantage of every contour. Where necessary they would be carried on rude trestles across small valleys and watercourses. Once they reached the large rivers the logs were bound together and floated in dozens, locally known as ' tylters.'

During the Middle Ages and up to the eighteenth century Norway was one of the principal sources from which Holland obtained her timber supplies. The Dutch were clever engineers, and some time during the sixteenth century were the first people to erect mechanical frame-saws driven by both wind and water. Many of these mills stood around the mouth of the Rhine. The demand from Holland was for " Dutch balks" (long, thick, absolutely straight-hewn balks) to be sawn in these mills, but by the middle of the eighteenth century such timber was becoming increasingly difficult to find in Norway. At first it was only Western Sweden, and in particular Gothenburg, that benefited by using Norwegian methods. In the eighteenth century water-driven sawmills were erected by Gothenburg merchants, in particular at Lilla Edet. Among the pioneer sawmill owners was an Englishman named John Hall. Later he was followed by his compatriots David Carnegie, William Gibson, B. C. Hichens, and the Dickson Brothers. Up to nearly the middle of the

nineteenth century the timber trade was handicapped by the fact
that sawmills might not legally be erected in any area where
they would compete with the favoured iron-mines which used
wood for smelting.

Sawmilling in Southern Sweden remained very backward
during this period. Saw-blades forged by blacksmiths were held

EARLY WATER-DRIVEN SWEDISH FRAME-SAW
AB Text and Bilder, Stockholm. By courtesy of the Swedish Wood Exporters' Association.

in crude wooden frames driven by water-mills. From 1740
onward the Government tried to encourage fine-bladed saws,
but by 1825 there were still only 68 of these in the whole country,
compared with 472 coarse-bladed saws in Norrland alone. The
average sawn-wood production of fine-bladed saws was many
times that of the older variety, and in addition their operators
were entitled to fell trees at a very low fee. In Upper Norrland
sawing by hand for export was still practised at the beginning
of the nineteenth century. As a matter of fact, exporters often

preferred the products of skilled hand-sawyers using fine rolled-steel saws in comparison with the primitive hand-forged, water-driven frame-saws. The numerous English firms engaged at an early date in the Swedish wood trade must remind us of the commercial Treaty signed in 1654 between Oliver Cromwell and " The Lady Christina, by the grace of God, Queen of the Swedes, Goths and Vandales, great prince of Finland, duke of Esthonia, Carelia, Bremen, Veherden, Stetin, Pomerland, Cassubia and Vandalia, prince of Rugia, and lady of Ingrie and of Wismer." These illustrious titles are given in full to show the enormous area of forest territory controlled by Sweden in the sixteenth and seventeenth centuries. Articles of the Treaty recite that :

> It shall be lawfull for the subjects and inhabitants of the kingdome of Sweden to travell into all the countreys of England, Scotland and Ireland, and likewise to passe beyond land or sea, and other people that commerce with them, to exercise trade in all kind of merchandise, and to bring them thither, and carry thence att their pleasure. The people of the aforesaid commonwealth shall injoy the same liberty in the kingdomes, dominions and territories of the queene and kingdome of Sweden ; but, upon condition that they shall observe the respective lawes, ordinances, and particular rights of both nations, and of those things which concerne the traficque. . . . It is thought fitt that the shippers, waggons, marchandies and men belonging to one of the confaederates, in their journeys and navigations, shall be armed with letters of safe conduct, commonly called passeports and certificates, which shall be signed by the chiefe governor or magistrate of the province or citty from whence they come.

Up to 1800 the ownership of forest-lands in Sweden was confused, the Crown claiming all forests that " could not with good reason be fully proved to belong to some estate, village, parish or hundred." This formula might seem to indicate very large Crown forest-lands. But when at the commencement of the nineteenth century a policy of exact delimitation was pursued it was found that the demands of local proprietors, villages, iron-works, etc., were so clamant that the Crown territories in settled districts became severely curtailed. In fact, Crown forests were established largely only in areas hitherto sparsely inhabited and undeveloped. It was the Riksdag which in the early years of

the nineteenth century passed a number of laws settling the forest
boundaries, particularly in the provinces of Dalarne, Gävleborg,
Västernorrland, and Jämtland. Undoubtedly the expansion of
the Swedish timber industry in the nineteenth century brought
about the demand for a more exact delimitation of forest ownership. Up to that time the Swedish Government had concerned
itself chiefly with the protection and furtherance of the iron trade.

During the earlier centuries Swedish timber exports were on
a comparatively moderate scale, although some cargoes were
carried far afield, for instance, to the Mediterranean, Spain, and
even the Spanish Colonies in South America. The Government
paid an annual subsidy to the notorious Barbary pirate chiefs,
located in Algiers, for the safe-conduct of ships flying the Swedish
flag in the Mediterranean. It was the custom to employ small
vessels on these Southern voyages during the winter months,
when they would have been icebound in Northern waters.
Enterprising sawmillers would combine with ship-owners to
send wood cargoes on consignment to such ports as Rio de
Janeiro, Puerto Rico, and Port of Spain. Quite often the wooden
ships were built and voyaged with a cargo of timber with the
express intention of selling both the vessel and its cargo at the
port of arrival.

Until the middle of the nineteenth century the wood exported from Sweden consisted of approximately equal quantities
of hewn and sawn timber. The hewn timber came principally
from ports in Sundsvall, Småland, and Gotland. For this purpose the logs were floated down the rivers to the coast, and then
roughly squared by hand in what were known as ' balk-pits.'
However, hewn timber could not be shipped without a quantity
of deals to pack the ship's hold, and consequently sawn wood
was purchased by the exporter to make up his cargoes. Much
of these sawn goods were produced in peasant sawmills against
small cash advances by the coast merchants. It was a seasonal
occupation for the small farmers, and both the hauling of the
logs and the sawing were done in the long Northern winter.
Frequently the timber merchant would undertake the payment
of the farmer's taxes and deduct the amount from the cash
settlement made to the latter on his rare visits to the town to
purchase his family's requirements.

A considerable drawback to this method of trading was that

the bulk of the sawn deals and battens had to be roughly rafted and floated down the swift-flowing rivers to the ports. Hence the wood became discoloured and grey and lost that ' bright ' appearance. To meet this difficulty a number of merchants and exporters established large water-driven sawmills at the ports or at other points where the rivers became less turbulent and were navigable for small sea-going vessels. The enterprising traders of Gothenburg were early in the field. A dozen water sawmills were established below the Trollhättan rapids, south of Lake Vänern, while in Värmland, at Munkfors, Dejefors, and Edsvalla, there were other mills. The sawn wood from these Gothenburg enterprises was well sawn, and, above all, ' bright,' being loaded straight to ship, without being floated, and consequently it commanded a ready market.

After the coming of steam-power to the south, water-driven mills survived in the Norrland province for many years. Even in the 1860's, when the new steam-driven mills were being erected in large numbers, there were to be found old-established enterprises which went on enlarging their water-driven sawmills to meet the increased demand, rather than write off their capital investments and turn to the new ways. There were large water-driven mills at Mo, Brannfors, Kvarnfors, Matfors, and Askesta, among other places. Established as they were by local business families, by 1860 most of these sawmills had come into the hands of Stockholm and Gothenburg merchant houses. It is evident that before the great export expansion of the second half of the nineteenth century the timber trade in Norrland was a chancy business at best. Small traders had to strain their resources by cash advances to the farmer and peasant producers, while at the receiving end their agents abroad were apt to default.

A typical trader of limited resources, at any rate at the outset, who did make good was T. F. Heffner. A Swede, the son of a Ronneby artisan, he left home and took an engagement with a Hull timber merchant. Soon after 1820 this firm sent him back to Sundsvall. Starting by trading for his English employer, he soon set up an independent exporting business, and as the timber trade improved in 1840 his fortunes rose with it, so that he became a wealthy citizen. A cautious yet far-seeing business-man, he invested his savings in small water sawmills and the purchase of forest-lands. However, it is said that even he, at the age of seventy, became a convert to the new steam-power, in spite of the initial cost of its installation. According to Heffner's letters, he considered that three sawmills driven by water-wheels could be bought for the price of a single steam-operated mill. Nevertheless it was the coming of steam, combined with a single political factor, that brought wealth and power to Sweden's timber industry.

This was the relaxation of Great Britain's tariff policy in the middle years of the nineteenth century. In 1851 the duty on foreign-sawn timber was reduced to 33*s.* per standard, with hewn timber at 7*s.* 6*d.* per load. Colonial timber was admitted practically free. By 1860 the rate of duty on all timber from whatever source was fixed at one shilling per load, while in 1866 this nominal duty was repealed and timber was free. Almost immediately Great Britain appeared as a buyer on the Baltic market on a hitherto unprecedented scale. Between 1846 and 1850 the average value of all timber exports from Sweden amounted to some 6 million rix dollars (£1 sterling equals approximately 18 rix dollars). For the five years following the abolition of the tariffs—*i.e.,* 1866 to 1870—the average annual value of exported Swedish timber rose to no less than 64 million rix dollars, a thousand per cent. increase. Of this total export Great Britain took approximately half, about £1,500,000 worth, consisting both of hewn and sawn goods, at an average price all over of approximately £10 per standard—let us say, 150,000 standards. By 1872 the total export to all countries had reached the handsome total of 550,000 standards.

Much of the increased production of sawn timber in the decade 1850 to 1860 was secured from the traditional water-driven saws. Professor Gardlund has shown that as late as 1860 there were only seventeen steam sawmills in the province of Norrland, while of sizable water-driven sawmills there were several hundred still at work. There is no doubt that it was the demand of the expanding British market for ' bright,' well-sawn goods that provided the main impulse to erect steam-driven sawmills. As pointed out earlier, most of these were sited at the point of export, either at ports or on navigable waters. It has been said that during the 1850's British agents did their best to convince their customers that river-floated timber was just as serviceable as the new ' bright ' wood, but their hard-headed customers would not listen. Consequently, by the 1860's floated timber became virtually unsaleable in Great Britain, although still acceptable in France. These factors induced many exporters of hewn timber to change over to the business of producing sawn timber. Naturally it seemed reasonable to these newcomers

SAWMILL AND TIMBER WHARF AT SKUTSKÄR, SWEDEN (*circa* 1860)
By courtesy of the Swedish Wood Exporters' Association.

to start with the new steam sawmills. By 1875 there were seventy-five sawmills in Norrland.

A company of Sundsvall exporters erected the first steam sawmill in Sweden at Tunadad in 1849. The second, erected by Mr Bunsav in 1851, was located on the Baltic island of Mön. Frequently Norwegian managers and technical experts were engaged to assist in running these new ventures. For some reason Norway was technically and industrially better equipped than Sweden up to the middle of the nineteenth century. Things are, of course, different to-day. The district of Gothenburg was largely responsible for the increase in exports for the five years following 1850. Not only did the merchants work their own

SAWMILL WITH LOG RAFTS AT ASKESTA, SWEDEN (1870)

By courtesy of the Swedish Wood Exporters' Association.

T.—7

mills, but they financed and exported the production of many small up-country water sawmill owners. For this purpose they had the assistance of credits from importing firms in England, France, and Holland. Gothenburg had a well-merited reputation for commercial probity. In fact, the city acquired the nickname of " Little London." In a time of considerable trade expansion the Gothenburg newspapers would attack speculators almost in the tone of *The Times* of that day.

Typical merchants of those days were Dickson and Co., Wilhelm Rohss and Co., and J. A. Kjelberg and Sons. The Dickson firm was founded by two English immigrants, brothers whose Christian names were Robert and James. They were said to be the real pioneers of the Swedish timber export trade. They bought forests and water sawmills in Värmland, at Munk-fors, Dejefors, and Edsvalla, greatly extending the productions of these undertakings. With great foresight in the 1820's, they bought still more forests in Norrland, often very cheaply indeed. It has been recorded that in Upper Norrland they purchased extensive forest territories at 70 ore, or 9*d.*, an acre. The Dicksons soon reaped the benefits of these latter investments, for by 1855 Gothenburg as a great timber-exporting centre began to fall behind in the race. This firm then sold out their Värmland interests and concentrated their great export enterprises in Norr-land. Among English agent firms active in those early days were Churchill and Sim, and Foy, Morgan, and Co.

The twenty-five years from 1875 to the Boer War in 1899 was the period of consolidation of the Swedish wood industry. Production, mainly of sawn goods, and consumption remained high, but prices fell. The last quarter of the nineteenth century in Europe has been summarized by economists as the time of the " Great Depression." The middle of the century had been famous for a great outburst of commercial and industrial expan-sion. Much new plant of great productive capacity had been installed, and bank credit largely expanded. Now a reaction set in. Prices in all commodities dropped, and profits were reduced to meet the times. The Swedish timber trade was no exception to the general trend. From 1875 onward for ten years prices sagged. At the first open water in 1874 prices for English sawn goods averaged £15 10*s.* per standard for joinery wood, and £11 for carcassing, these being the highest ever obtained.

However, in 1885, when the bottom was reached, quite good productions could be bought for £12 per standard, while carcassing timber fell to £5 per standard.

The Swedish Wood Exporters' Association was founded on November 6, 1875, at a meeting in Stockholm. Messrs H. R. Astrup, J. E. Francke, and Wilhelm Rohss were elected as the first committee. They represented the class of big exporters and financiers. There is no doubt that it was the onset of the " Great Depression " that led to the formation of the Association. While trade was booming all was well, but the recession brought on a crop of credit troubles, financial failures, and not least complaints and claims from the hard-hit customers. The Swedish sawmillers, merchants, and exporters felt the need to combine and show a united front to the outside world. In 1883 the Association reached its first agreement for an agreed limitation of output, and in consequence the following year saw a 10-per-cent. fall in exports. Limitations on output were tried several times in the years down to 1896, when the world economic depression began to lift. Sweden's exports of timber in 1900 totalled 1,007,000 standards, and by 1913 had risen to 1,046,000 standards.

However, her pre-eminence as Europe's chief timber exporter had passed with the century, for by 1913 Russian exports had risen to 1,455,000 standards of sawn timber, and so took first place. The reasons for this change are not simply or easily analysed. No doubt by this time Sweden's forest wealth had been under increasingly heavy pressure for two centuries, whereas Russia still possessed virtually primeval forests. The trees available to Swedish sawmills tended to get smaller and smaller. Up to 1860 no timber was brought to the mills under 10″ diameter top measure. It is said that when the sawmills commenced to buy forests in Västerbotten no lesser logs were taken unless they were of exceptional quality. Under the expanding demand there was a relaxation by 1880 to 8″ top diameter, while by the arrival of the twentieth century logs of top diameters of 6″ or even less became a common sight in the mill-ponds. Further, the rapid development of the pulp trade provided a remunerative market for the smaller logs available, consequently there was no pressure to convert them into sawn wood, and therefore the export surplus fell.

By and large, it might be reasonably said that the opening years of the twentieth century down to the First World War were comfortable times for the Swedish timber trade. It is true that there was this difficulty of obtaining sufficient sizable logs, but the mills made the necessary technical adjustments to deal with the smaller wood, and selling prices remained firm. Planed goods tended to rise in quantity at the expense of sawn wood, and between 1900 and 1913 the former increased from 12 per cent. to 24 per cent. of the whole. Redwood always preponderated in the unplaned timber. There was a considerable fall in the British proportion of the exports. This was 44 per cent. in 1900, but only 30 per cent. in 1913. It is said that the Swedish exporters found business with the smaller customers, such as Holland, Belgium, Denmark, etc., more profitable.

The outbreak of war in 1914 and the action of the German Navy freed Sweden from her Baltic competitors. At the outset her timber exports to the Allied and neutral countries were well maintained, but later the unrestricted German submarine campaign brought grave shipping difficulties. By 1918 the f.o.b. value of timber had doubled, but its c.i.f. value in Great Britain had quadrupled to £60 or £70 per standard, chiefly due to the steep rise in freight charges. The Swedish sawmills and exporters made good profits during the early part of the War, but later on their difficulties increased, due to both rising costs and falling exports. However, the Armistice of November 11, 1918, put an entirely changed complexion on things. There was an immediate world demand for timber, of which Sweden, together with all the other exporting countries, took full advantage. By 1919 prices had reached an all-time high ! However, Nemesis was waiting round the corner. The following year the post-war slump set in, and by 1921 Swedish wood exports were down to the lowest figure since 1870. The slump was not of long duration, and timber exports were soon rising again ; by 1927 they were over one million standards, of which Great Britain received approximately 400,000 standards. Our country was still by far the most important market for timber in the world. In 1929 the export of boxboards reached its highest figure at 87,000 standards. Later production declined as the use of other packing materials such as hard and soft board increased.

In 1931 the great depression blew across the Atlantic, and

the Swedish timber trade immediately reacted. For two years
total exports were down below 800,000 standards, and prices
fell to match. A slow recovery then took place : both production and prices rose. It was out of these troublesome times that
the European Timber Exporters' Convention (E.T.E.C.) was

GIANT TIMBER RAFT BEING TOWED ACROSS THE BALTIC (1918)
By courtesy of the Swedish Wood Exporters' Association.

born. Founded in November 1935 at Copenhagen, its members
were Sweden, Finland, the U.S.S.R., Poland, Czechoslovakia,
Austria, Jugoslavia, and Roumania. The Convention was
directed by an Executive Committee of six members, whose
duty was to seek the co-operation of the various member countries. The purpose of E.T.E.C. was to limit production by means
of quotas. This it successfully did until the outbreak of war in
the autumn of 1939. The production of all the Swedish sawmills was, however, 14 per cent. less in 1939 than at the commencement of the decade, while the total exports of timber

declined by 28 per cent. This decline was due to a number of causes, such as the shortage of suitable logs and the restrictions of import in many wood-consuming industries.

It is not until the end of the eighteenth century that any clear picture emerges of the timber trade in Russia. The Hanseatic merchants from Wisby and the Livonian ports penetrated as far as Novgorod in the thirteenth century. At that time the great Muscovite city on the Volga was an independent trading republic. The Hanse established a flourishing counting house here, and in exchange for the manufactures of the West exported through the North Baltic ports timber, hides, furs, and corn. Water-driven sawmills were first established by foreign concessionnaires, and later, when Russian merchants took an interest, foreigners were brought in as managers and technicians. Here is an extract from a report by a high Russian forest official, M. Judrae, who made a tour of the St Petersburg (now Leningrad) district in 1867. His account of the quite considerable output obtained from water-driven machinery is very illuminating :

> At a distance of ninety versts, or sixty miles, from Petrozavodsk, is the village of Leejma, where there is a saw-mill of considerable magnitude, occupied also at the present time by M. Baelaeff. It is erected on the river Leejma, and has two water-wheels and four frames of saws, two for each water-wheel. It works without intermission day and night, and can cut up in the course of the year 60,000 logs ; but, in consequence of the hindering of circumstances, it cuts up only some 45,000. These are pine logs of the length of twenty-two feet, and eight vershooks or fourteen inches thick at the upper extremity. The boards most in demand in the market are twenty-two feet long, and three inches thick, which are known as $2\frac{1}{2}$ in. boards ; and besides these there are what are called inch boards, sent chiefly to Holland. According to the statements of the traders these inch boards are both in quality and price inferior to the Swedish boards of the same measurement, in consequence of which the preparation of them in large quantities is not remunerative.

A foreign merchant's life in Russia in the 1850's seems to have had its thrills. Here is a vivid account by Mr Hepworth Dixon of a journey he made southward from Archangel in a tarantass. This was a wooden cart consisting mainly of two pairs of wheels set some ten feet apart. On the axles was lashed a sort of raft of wooden poles, and to the platform so achieved was attached the body of the vehicle, a primitive wooden shell. Over all was a rough canvas tylt. It had the great advantage of being easily repaired after the inevitable breakdown on the atrocious roads. However, let Mr Dixon tell his own story :

> A private tarantass is brought round to the gate ; an empty shell, into which they toss our luggage, first the hard pieces—hat-box, gun-case, trunk ; then piles of hay to fill up chinks and holes, and wisps of straw to bind the mass ; on all which they lay your bedding, coats, and skins. A woodman's axe, a coil of rope, a ball of string, a bag of nails, a pot of grease, a basket of bread and wine, a joint of roast-beef, a teapot, and a case of cigars, are after-wards coaxed into the nooks and crannies of the shell. Starting at dusk, so as to reach the ferry at which we are to cross the river by daybreak, we splash the mud and grind the planks of Archangel beneath our hoofs. " Goodbye ! Look out for wolves ! Take care of brigands ! Goodbye ! goodbye ! " shout a dozen voices ; and then that friendly and frozen city is left behind. All night under murky stars we tear along a dreary path ; pines on our right, pines on our left, and pines in our front. We bump through a village, waking up houseless dogs ; we reach a ferry, and pass the river on a raft ; we grind over stones and sand ; we tug through slush and bog ; all night, all day ; all night again, and after that all day, winding through the maze of forest leaves, now turned and scared and swirled on every blast that blows. Each day of our drive is like its fellow. A clearing thirty yards wide runs out before us for a thousand versts, the pines are all alike, the birches all alike. The villages are still more alike each other than the trees.

In 1873 a Mr Werekka prepared a report on Russia's forestry and timber industries for the great International Exhibition at Vienna. At that time it is clear that much of the sawing, even for export, was still done by hand. Mr Werekka reckoned that there were in Russia some hundred great sawmills, of which only thirty were driven by steam. Archangel possessed six steam sawmills, all of which were sawing for England. The whole of these mills converted about two millions of trees annually. The small water-mills were mainly engaged in sawing for local requirements. Fifty of the larger water sawmills and all the steam mills were judged to be working for the export trade. British timber interests were among the first to seek concessions in the great forest territories surrounding the White Sea. That

indefatigable traveller Mr Hepworth Dixon gives the following
account of the port of Archangel about 1860 :

> Climbing up the river you come upon fleets of rafts and praams,
> on which you may observe some part of the native life. The rafts
> are floats of timber—pine logs, lashed together with twigs of
> willow, capped with a tent of planks in which the owner sleeps,
> while his woodmen lie about in the open air when they are not
> paddling the raft or guiding it down the stream. These rafts come
> down the Dvina and its feeders for a thousand miles. Cut in the
> great forests of Vologda and Nijni Konetz, the pines are dragged
> to the waterside, and knitted by rude hands into these broad, float-
> ing masses. At the towns more sturdy helpers can be hired for
> nothing ; many of the poor peasants being anxious to get down
> the river on their way to the shrine of Solovetsk. For a passage
> on the raft these pilgrims take a turn at the oar, and help the owners
> to guide her through the shoals.

An English concessionnaire working the forests in the Olonetz
Province was the Onega Timber Company. Most of their sawmills were in the neighbourhood of the town of Onega. They
were said to be financed by a group of British capitalists engaged
almost exclusively in the timber trade. By 1874 the company
had a contract with the Russian Government valid for twenty
years to fell not fewer than 60,000 or more than 200,000 trees
in any one year. Their concession area extended from the
northern end of Lake Latcha along the banks of the river Onega,
and covered all the tributaries of this river from its source to its
mouth. The biggest trees were said to grow round Lake Latcha.
The Onega Timber Company were bound at the beginning of
each season to make an advance payment of 55 kopecs per tree
on the quantity they planned to fell. Thus every autumn they
would pay to the Government between 50,000 and 60,000 roubles.

It was the custom of the Onega Timber Company to sub-
contract their felling, not to individuals, but to peasant families.
These would fell the trees and drag the logs with their ponies
over the winter snows to the banks of streams and small rivers.
In the spring along would come a contractor called the " Splavt-
chick," or floater. With his men he would push the logs into
the water and ' drive ' the river until the logs were gathered in
the great booms opposite the sawmills. The forestry regulations
demanded that no tree should be felled higher than one arshine,

or 28 in., above the ground on penalty of twice the value of the tree. The Onega Timber Company owned three steam sawmills besides numerous water-driven mills. The sawing was done with great care and with due regard to the English and French markets. The purchase price or royalty worked out at 1s. 4½d. per tree. It is recorded that the Onega Timber Company, after paying all their expenses, used to realize profits in the neighbour-hood of 33 per cent. annually. Another British firm working the forests in the Onega area were Messrs Thornton. They owned a number of sawmills on the river Onega, but their principal steam mill was on an island at the mouth of the river. Here in the summer seagoing vessels drawing 25 ft. could anchor alongside the wharf to load direct from the storage-sheds. On the river connecting Lake Onega with Lake Ladoga lies the river port of Ladonoi Pole. It was here that Peter the Great built his first wooden galleys. It will be remembered that the stout King learnt the shipwright's trade personally at the dockyards of Deptford. These galleys, the earliest Russian fleet, were used to take the fort of Schlüsselburg, on the Gulf of Finland, from the Swedes. The logs were brought down the river in great rafts. It is recorded that these timber floats were largely worked by women, even down to the middle of the nineteenth century.

CHAPTER VII

AMERICA ; U.S.A.

AMERICAN lumbermen like to talk about their timber
business as the oldest export trade from the shores of
North America. Certainly lumbering dates back to the
Virginia Company, granted its first Charter on April 10, 1606.
There are some, however, who would date the earliest exploitation of timber in the New World to A.D. 1000, relying for their
source upon the Norse saga of Eric the Red, which tells how Leif
Ericsson brought a cargo of wood from " Vinland " to the Norsemen's settlements in Greenland. A hundred years later another
saga tells of the trading voyages of Thorfinn Karlsefne, who
sailed west and loaded his long, narrow ships with wood for
Iceland and Greenland. Besides "Vinland," the territory of
" Markland " is also mentioned in these early Norse chronicles
as being a heavily forested district. The frequent occurrences
in the northern sagas of references to forests and woods, obviously
quite foreign to conditions in Greenland, are in themselves very
strong presumptive evidence that the Norsemen actually reached
the wooded coasts of North America. Probably in the first
place quite by accident rather than by design, their ships were
blown off their course by the great autumn gales to make a
landfall many leagues to the west. Hardy sailors as they were,
one could imagine their having at least a sporting chance of
bringing their staunch vessels safely home to Greenland the
following spring. Once the trail had been blazed, succeeding
voyages would be planned and made in more favourable circumstances to bring back the timbers so scarce in Greenland. To
return to the Virginia Company and the days of documented
history, it is recorded that among the persons accompanying the
second expedition under Captain Newport in 1608 were eight
Poles and Dutchmen specifically engaged for their skill in erecting
sawmills. It is probable that the first sawmill was erected in
the principal settlement of Jamestown. In the same year the
redoubtable Captain Smith is found reporting to England
that the country was greatly overgrown with pine. John

Chamberlain, an English diarist, writes in 1609 of Captain Newport's return voyage :

> There is likewise a ship newly come from Virginia with some pretty commodities and hope of more, as divers sorts of wood for wainscot and other uses, soap-ashes, some pitch and tar, certain unknown kinds of herbs for dying, not without suspicion as they term it of cochineal.

In the state of Maine it is said that a sawmill was built at York in 1623, while an inscription records that a sawmill was erected in 1634 at South Berwick. The date of 1634 is very circumstantial, as it is recorded that the good ship *Pied Cow* carried a sawmill from England to Maine on her voyage in that year. In 1605 Captain George Weymouth, R.N., brought back samples of pine woods from the Virginian Colony, and his name stands commemorated in Weymouth Pine. Such was the pressing demand for masts and spars that an export trade in these commodities rapidly developed. In 1609 William Strachey tells us that the good ship *Starre* actually carried eighty Virginia Pine masts and a number of lesser spars. Contemporary reports say the English shipwrights were amazed at their quality. The Virginia Company's minutes state that in 1620 " with great care and cost there were procured men skilful in sawing mills from Hambrough." This latter town is presumably Hamburg ! Until its charter was cancelled in 1624 the Company was active in making clapboards for building the local coast ships and in producing pitch, tar, and resin for making them seaworthy. Mr William Strachey, the first Secretary of Jamestown, wrote home to his masters in London, describing the Virginian forests as follows :

> The oake here, for stature and tymber, may compare with any, being so tall and streight, that they will beare 4 square of good tymber for twenty yardes long . . . there is also elme and ash, of which are made sope-ashes . . . of walnutts there be three kindes, the black walnutt, which is returned home yearly by all shipping from thence and yields good profit, for yt is well bought up to make waynscott, tables, cubbordes, chaires, and stools, of a delicate grayne and cullour like ebonie, and not subject to the worms. . . .

In 1623 a cargo of white pine boards is recorded as having been shipped to England from Plymouth, in Massachusetts, while a Dutch boat, *The Arms of Amsterdam*, in 1626 brought oak timber and hickory from the New Netherlands to Holland. The Colony of Massachusetts as early as 1648 enacted a law to forbid the lighting of fires in enclosures in dry spells, and an offender was to be fined or whipped. The incoming settlers were only too ready to fire the forest to effect clearings, while the Indians left their camp-fires burning without thought of the consequences. Further, the Indian custom was to plan " fire hunts." Several hundred braves would take part in such a hunt. After locating a large herd of deer they would light a number of fires around the doomed animals, and as the flames converged the terrified deer would endeavour to break out of the fiery circle, only to fall an early prey to the waiting hunters.

The provision of timber, pitch, and resin for H.M. ships was an outstanding duty of the Government, and in 1698, in the reign of William and Mary, the Board of Trade and Plantations, with its office in London, sent a Commission under Mr John Bridger to investigate the possibilities of North America. Following the Commission's Report, Parliament passed in 1705 an Act for the encouragement of the importation of naval stores from the American plantations. Bounties were to be paid on masts, pitch, tar, and turpentine. Under the Admiralty Board, once the delight of Mr Samuel Pepys, it was the custom for Naval Contractors in London to employ " mast Agents " in the American Colonies to oversee the production of the stores. The mast agents in their turn engaged local contractors to cut the trees and haul the masts to the nearest port or landing-stage. Such a mast agent was William Partridge, a merchant residing in Portsmouth, New Hampshire. In 1694 he entered into a contract with one Captain Thomas Harvey of Massachusetts Bay, stipulating that the latter was to provide :

> 10,000 feet of good merchantable ore rafters of white ash from fifteen to twenty-two feet long and three score tons of good merchantable white oak knees and standards, square, not less than five feet.

Captain Harvey received £101 10s. for the timber, which was to be delivered to a good landing-stage on the Merriman river, where it could be loaded into ocean-going ships. If either party failed in its duties under the contract two hundred pounds current money of New England was to be paid as forfeit. Such was the concern of the Admiralty Board that in 1705 Mr John Bridger, mentioned above as Chief Commissioner, was appointed Surveyor-General of Her Majesty's Woods in North America. His duties included : protecting the forests from both the elements and the settlers ; improving the quality of the masts and timbers shipped to the Royal Dockyards ; marking the trees and keeping a register of mast trees. Such trees were marked by a hatchet-stroke with a " broad arrow." To carry out his onerous duties the Surveyor-General was provided by the Massachusetts Court with a galley, a working party of twenty-eight men, and a military guard. At first the office was popular with Colonial Governors and assemblies, who hoped that a profitable trade in naval stores could be developed with the Mother Country. Later the Colonial merchants and lumbermen came to resent the restrictions on their liberties imposed by the British Government regulations dictated from London. In spite of the prohibition, cargoes of prime timber were shipped away to the West Indies, Spain, Portugal, and even France. A Navy Contractor was Ralph Gulston of London. He contracted in 1726 with Samuel Waldo, a mast agent of Boston, and Colonel Thomas Westbrook, a New Hampshire plantation owner, for six shiploads of masts, yards, and bowsprits. The transaction is recorded because the contractors applied to the Massachusetts Government for troops to protect their workmen and teams of over a hundred oxen from attacks by the local Indians. A corporal and ten soldiers were supplied at a total charge of £114 10s. 4d. to protect the petitioners and their servants in their business of " masting the Royal Navy according to His Majesty's Royal Licence." The trees were felled in the autumn and dragged out when the ground was covered with ice and snow. Iced roads were made, and the great mast trees hauled out on sleds drawn by oxen. A giant mast, worth, say, a hundred pounds, would require twenty yoke of oxen to drag it to the river-bank. Special vessels known as ' mast ships ' were built to carry masts, usually of about five hundred tons burthen. They were provided with special entry ports at bow and stern, through which the long spars were hauled aboard. (In the year 1666 King Charles II had received a special gift of two great pine masts from the Colony of Massachusetts as " a testimony of loyalty and affection " from the Assembly.) So far we have dealt principally with the more northerly Colonies, but we now come to an interesting Statute enacted by the South Carolina Assembly in 1712 :

In this province the number of inhabitants being so few for so great extent of land, the erecting of mills of all kinds and other

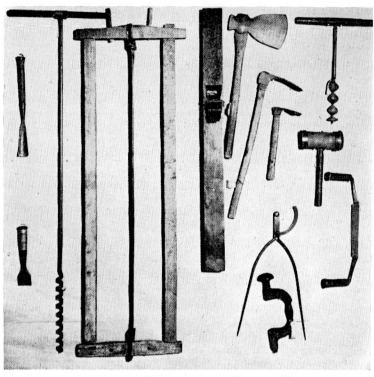

TOOLS USED FOR SHIPBUILDING IN COLONIAL TIMES
By courtesy of the Essex Institute of Salem, Mass.

mechanic engines will greatly improve the country itself, and its trade and navigation ; Be it therefore enacted by the authority aforesaid, that whatever person or persons shall, after the ratification of this Act, erect a mill to saw with the wind or water, so as to bring the same to complete perfection as in Holland or in other countrys, he or they shall have the privilege of wind or water sawmills in this part of this province, exclusive of all others, for the term of 8 years after the first sawmill begins to work.

All this time the lumber drive was from the Atlantic Coast ever westward. The first sawmill in the Appalachians was constructed in 1776 by one John Minear in the Tucker County of West Virginia. It was a sash mill, and stood on a tributary of the river Cheat, which supplied the necessary water-power. A sash saw was so called because of the vertical frame or sash which held the single saw-blade, frequently hand-forged by the local smith. The feed was driven by a primitive form of ratchet, five hundred feet of sawing being a good day's work. It is said that the feed was so slow that the early farmer-cum-sawmiller could easily plough an acre or so between cuts, but this may be an exaggeration ! By 1835, according to Martin's *Gazetteer of Virginia and District of Columbia*, forty sawmills were working in West Virginia ; all were water-driven, and even as late as 1860 only a few steam-powered mills had been erected. It was not till after the Civil War that steam became the general motive-power in Virginia.

The U.S.A. had just fought a desperate war to secure her independence, and her citizens were quick to defend their freshly won liberty. Surely this advertisement, published in Salem, Massachusetts, in 1798, would stir the mind of any timber-owning patriot and cause him to hurry his best White Oak trees down to the shipyard :

The Salem Frigate

TAKE NOTICE !

Ye Sons of Freedom ! all true lovers of the Liberty of your Country! step forth, and give your assistance in building the Frigate, to oppose French insolence and piracy. Let every man in possession of a White Oak Tree, be ambitious to be foremost in hurrying down the timber to Salem, and fill the complement wanting, where the noble structure is to be fabricated, to maintain your rights upon the Seas, and make the name of America respected among the nations of the world. Your largest and longest trees are wanted, and the arms of them for Knees and Rising Timber. Four trees are wanted for the Keel, which all together will measure 146 feet in length, and hew 16 inches square. Please to call on the Subscriber, who wants to make contracts for large or small quantities, as may suit best, and will pay the READY CASH.

ENOS BRIGGS

SALEM, *Nov.* 23, 1798

The South—that is to say, the area below the famous Mason-Dixon line—recovered quickly following the cessation of the

War of Independence. Cotton and tobacco boomed, and the lumber industry expanded rapidly to supply the demand for building and constructional material. In the census of 1810 it is recorded that there were sixty-five sawmills in South Carolina, one sawmill in Georgia produced alone 1,252,000 feet per annum, while thirty-four sawmills in the territory of New Orleans produced together 6,790,000 feet in the year. At the close of the eighteenth century it was the custom in Florida to make " mill grants " of five miles square of forest-land to encourage the erection of water sawmills. Such a grant was made in 1801 to two citizens of St Augustine to build a sawmill " at the head of the Creek of Moultrie." The state of Georgia was particularly favoured by having a number of ports, such as Savannah, Darien, and Brunswick, standing at the mouths of rivers reaching back to the pine-clad interior. By 1841 her export trade in lumber had reached 14 million board feet, and this had grown to 50 million board feet by 1861. One of the earliest hardwood mills operating in the South, and certainly the most historic, stood on St Simons Island, Savannah, near to the shipyards. Here in 1797 the sawmiller John Couper cut the frames and timbers for the famous U.S. frigate *Constitution*, launched on October 20 of that year, and later a thorn in the side of the British in the war of 1812. It is very interesting indeed that one of the earliest saw-milling companies in the " solid South " was established and operated for over a hundred years by a coloured family. John Hilton, a coloured man, in 1825 built a water-driven whipsaw mill at Chapin, Lexington, South Carolina. His son Dennis took over from the old man, and in 1873 installed a steam circular saw. In 1888 the Company moved its mills to Louisville.

Up to 1830 we have been talking of timbers hauled by oxen and horses to the nearest river or port. If no waterway was available within a short haul the wood could not be got. But now a magician appears on the scene in the person of the railway engineer and surveyor. Immediately literally millions of acres of hitherto unavailable forest territory were thrown open to exploitation. Initial construction saw short tracks built from interior points to the nearest water, whether sea or river. Such was the West Feliciana Railroad, given its Charter in 1831 to construct a railway from Woodville, in the state of Mississippi, to the river port of St Francisville, on the great Mississippi river, a distance of twenty-six miles. The Directors issued their first tariff in 1835, and a later tariff, dated 1840, gave specific rates from station to station for the following articles :

Whiskey, per barrel ; molasses, per barrel ; shingles, per M. ; lumber, per 100 feet ; all taking the same rate. This railroad is now a part of the Y. & M.V.

The old Vicksburg and Jackson Railroad and the Southern Mississippi Railroad both received their Charter in 1835. Many another short-haul road was chartered between 1835 and 1861. Then came the Civil War, and these early railways were left burnt and blackened wrecks, but they had done their work and taken the lumbermen many a mile into the hitherto inaccessible interior.

Cincinnati, with its large population of German origin, was a centre of the Mid-West lumber industry. As early as 1881 it was being confidently asserted that " the Queen City of the West is the most important lumber market in the world ! " The City Directory of 1840 records a sawmill near the Methodist Church owned by one Nathan Tanner. Strangely, at that time there were several shipyards in the city, on the banks of the Ohio, and no doubt Tanner's sawmill supplied them. Six years later Benjamin Badger owned a steam sawmill and lath factory near the Washington Brewery. At the same time John Geyer, another mill-owner, advertised that he had for sale " a full line of furniture, including upholstered sociables, chairs and so forth." " Sociables " were couches so contrived that the occupants could sit face to face, and thus converse at ease !

Louisville, on the river Ohio, was another great centre of the developing lumber industry. Logs were safely brought from the Upper Ohio into the spacious ' sloughs ' and ' chutes ' lying behind Towhead Island ; also from its tributaries the Kentucky, Licking, and Big Sandy rivers in Kentucky, from the Big and Little Kanawhas in West Virginia, and the Allegheny and Monongahela rivers in Pennsylvania. This picturesque list of rivers serves to demonstrate how dependent the early lumbermen were on water both to move their logs and drive their sawmills. The mill known as " Old Hickory " was a floating sawmill planted on a large, flat barge and moved up and down the river as circumstances demanded.

It appears that the timber firms of Berup and Oakes, and John S. Prince of St Paul, both supplied outfits and supplies to lumbering parties, payment being taken in logs for their saw-mills. Mr Daniel Stanchfield, a lumberman from Maine, oper-ated a store in 1849, and took logs in payment which he shipped down the Mississippi. Later on he became a logging super-intendent for the firm of Cushing and Steele, and undertook to stock all their mills with logs by contract. In 1850 he provided two million board feet of logs, but in 1851 he surpassed his last year's efforts by bringing out no fewer than three million feet. However, it was not a case of all work and no play for Mr Stanchfield.   Listen to this :

> While I was resting for a part of the summer of 1847, in St Louis, after the sale of my lumber, the heat became so intense that I decided to leave for my voyage up the river. Just then Capt. John Atchison, with his steamer Lynx, arrived from New Orleans, carrying a cargo of government supplies for Fort Snelling, and having on board a pleasure party for the same destination. I secured a stateroom and joined the party. They were all southerners ex-cepting myself, a jolly crowd of ladies and gentlemen. The captain of the boat supplied a brass band that played and entertained us all day, and then furnished string music to dance by in the evening. Thus the whole trip was spent in pleasure, and the time passed rapidly until we arrived at Fort Snelling.

By the middle of the nineteenth century New England, once the cradle of the North American lumber business, was losing her pre-eminence as a producer. No longer had she the timber to serve the rapidly expanding population which was spreading both south and west. Once Maine, New England's largest state, was known as the " Pine Tree State." Great drives of pine and spruce logs were boomed down the Penobscot, the Kennebec, the Androscoggin, the St John, and other Maine rivers. Much of the export trade was centred in Boston. The great exporting firms of those days were Skillings, Whitney, and Barnes ; Shepard and Morse ; and the Export Lumber Company. But by the end of the Civil War all this was changed, and Boston became an importer of timber ! Sons of the Maine lumber barons migrated to Michigan, to the Southern States, and as time went on beyond the great river Mississippi. The epic march to the West Coast had begun. " Downeasters " from

Maine, "Blue-noses" from Nova Scotia, "Canucks" from French Canada, Swedish and German lumbermen, all helped to carry the great timber frontier forward to the Pacific Ocean.

IMMIGRANTS CONSTRUCTING A SECTION-FRAMED HOUSE UNDER THE SUPERVISION OF AN ARCHITECT (*circa* 1850)

Note the tool-box and draughtsman's equipment.

By courtesy of the Metropolitan Museum of Art, New York.

The spring ' drive ' was the climax of the logging year. The lumbermen and their bosses had spent the winter in the woods, first felling and trimming the logs and then dragging them by various means to the river-bank. In their rough log cabins they had lived on salt pork and beans, bread and molasses, washed down by a saltpetre brew of tea which would have scorched the hide of a rhinoceros ! There was no talk of vitamins or cans of tinned fruit, as there is to-day. The men would while away the long, dark evenings by dancing in their heavy calked boots to a fiddle and singing sentimental ballads such as *The Jam on Garry's Rock*, of which the following is the first of a hundred-odd verses :

> Come all ye brave shanty boys, wherever you may be ;
> I would have you pay attention and listen unto me.
> I'll sing you of a shanty boy, so noble, true and brave
> Who broke the jam on Garry's Rock and filled a watery grave.

In 1847 Mr Stanchfield worked for Cushing, Rantoul, and Co., a Massachusetts group of bankers who financed Mr Steele, a local lumberman who held an extensive pine-forest concession at the Falls of St Anthony, on the Rum river. At first things did not go well, and all the pine logs accumulated for the building of the essential dam to store water to drive the mill were swept out into the mighty Mississippi one stormy winter's night. Mr Stanchfield, however, was not dismayed, and here he is talking to one Ard Godfrey, the millwright :

> " Mr Godfrey, why not cut the hardwood timber here for the dam ? I have built several dams in Maine out of poorer timber than this. It will cost less, and will make a better job. The plank can be had at St Croix Falls to make it tight, and the dam can be built this winter. Should you wait for pine timber, it will delay the improvements one year longer."

The provision of the pine logs for the first year's sawing was almost a military undertaking. The trees were bought from an Ojibwa chief named Hole-in-the-Day. The price asked was fifty cents a tree plus a present of a pony, five pairs of blankets, some calico and broadcloth. Then the whole outfit for logging had to be brought a hundred and fifty miles from St Croix Falls. Oxen were the means of transport. Once at the scene of action, it was possible to hire more oxen, together with horses, mules, and ponies, from the local farmers. The work was to be done in the winter, and the necessary sleds were soon put together by the carpenters and smiths. Altogether that winter one and a half million feet of logs were hauled to the river-bank, and successfully floated down-river to St Anthony in the spring. Meanwhile Mr Ard Godfrey, the millwright, had done his job : both the dam and sawmill were all ready for their first season's cut in the year 1846, just one year after Mr Stanchfield had pushed his canoe up the Mississippi to locate the pine. Later in the same year a gang sawmill and two shingle mills were erected, all the plants working night and day to supply lumber for the houses

PINE LOGS BEING SORTED INTO 'BOOMS' AT THE CONCLUSION OF THE RIVER RUN

Photo British Columbia Forest Service. By courtesy of Ralph W. Andrews.

of the immigrants, who, as Mr Stanchfield says, were flocking into the newly opened territory of Minnesota :

> When river navigation opened in 1849, on the first boats, immigration came in small armies. Every boat was full of passengers. The sawmills were all running to supply lumber to build houses for the newcomers, and this was continued through all the year, as long as navigation lasted. About half of the immigrants stopped at St Paul. Both towns doubled in houses and families.

By 1854 the total logs 'driven' down the Rum river amounted to 33,000,000 feet. But things did not always go smoothly, and in the spring of 1856, owing to the breaking of the great boom, more than half the hard-won logs went over the St Anthony Falls. The logs were scattered along the course of the river—some, we are told, going into "Cave Boom" above St Paul, some into "Pig's Eye Slough," and others into Lake Pepin. Ultimately about half the runaway logs were salvaged and sold to mills in the Southern markets. In 1856 Mr Stanchfield was appointed Surveyor-General of logs for his district of Minneapolis, and the Upper Mississippi. He was therefore responsible for organizing the great drives. By law he could not cut or manufacture lumber during his term of office.

Typical of these logging associations was the St Croix Boom Company, organized in 1857 with a capital of 25,000 dollars. The members were a number of sawmilling companies from Marine, Stillwater, Taylor's Falls, and Osceola. The first booms were built at the latter place. In 1866 the Company was re-organized, the capital increased to 50,000 dollars, and the booms moved to Stillwater. The officers of the Boom Company were well-paid and competent men, as they needed to be to handle the log-marks of all the different participants in the drive. It is said that over 2000 marks were in use on this river organization alone ! Every owner had to have his log-marks recorded or forfeit his stock. The law protected the ownership of all regis-tered marks. These great annual log drives were apt to cause much damage by flooding to riverside property and farmlands. Much litigation ensued both owing to the blocking of the river and the impeding of navigation. It is said that in one year the damages claimed amounted to 146,525 dollars. Disputes also arose as to the jurisdiction of the St Croix river, it being the boundary of two states. These were the days when pitched battles took place between rival gangs as to whose drives should have priority on the river, and thus reach the markets first. The arrival on time of its logs might make all the difference between the prosperity and bankruptcy of a mill. These were tough times, and the rivermen did not wear kid-gloves in their dealings with one another.

Indiana as a source of lumber production dates from the 1830's. Its specialities in those days were oak and walnut. Poplar came into fashion later. Memphis was to become one of the most renowned lumber centres in the United States, with over fifty mills. Meanwhile the Appalachian timber industry was developing apace. The oldest sawmill in the territory, a sash mill, was constructed at Parkersburg in 1825. When this mill was destroyed by fire in 1853 it was replaced by a circular saw, and later by one of the earliest band-mills in the territory. Long before the Civil War logs were rafted down both the river Ohio and its tributaries. In 1840 an entire raft of poplar logs is said to have been sold at Parkersburg for the handsome sum of fifty dollars, and half that in trade goods. These logs were sawn chiefly at mills situate at Louisville, Portsmouth, and Cincinnati. Subsequent to the Civil War Kentucky and Tennessee were the scenes of river logging operations on a hitherto unprecedented scale. In these forests the yellow poplar was king, and beautiful wood was extracted which has never been equalled since that time. Much of this poplar was rafted to mills at Nashville.

At first poplar was looked upon as an inferior wood, and up to the 1880's poplar logs could be purchased at the river-banks ready for floating at four dollars for 18″ to 24″ and six dollars for 24″ and up diameter. Much of it was sold in those days for wagon-boards and scantlings. Later it was distributed all over the Middle West as a general-utility wood. As it grew in popularity a number of lumbering firms in Nashville, Chattanooga, Louisville, and Cincinnati formed the Poplar Manufacturers' Association to protect their interests.

It is an interesting fact, and may not be generally known, that, following the Civil War, in the 1870's there was a walnut boom in the Eastern States. This included not only walnut furniture for both dining-rooms and bedrooms, but also a great deal of both monumental woodwork and panelling was made in walnut. Much of the so-called 'colonial' style chairs, tables, and bureaux dated from these times. It is difficult to realize that at the outset the walnut-tree grew in groves, and many mills cut nothing else. The principal supplies were found in the states of Indiana and Tennessee. Prices for lumber at mill averaged 75 dollars for F.A.S., 50 dollars for Common, and 30 dollars for Culls. By 1885 the fashion for walnut had run its course, and oak came into its own.

By now sawmilling technique was advancing apace to the help of the lumberman. Mr Clint Prescott, a sawmaker himself, has recorded that the progress of invention was from the hand-operated whipsaw to the first crude water-driven sash saw, then to the Muley saw, followed by the round or live gangsaw, the

circular saw, and lastly the original bandsaw, which was the forerunner of the giant band-mills, with all their subsidiary plant,
operated in the American lumbering industry to-day. Benjamin
Cummins, a blacksmith, made the first circular saw in the U.S.A.
at Bentville, New York State.   The earliest bandsaw to be erected
in America is credited to Mr J. R. Hoffman, a lumberman of
Fort Wayne, Indiana.   His saw revolved round an upper and a
lower wooden wheel, both mounted on a wrought-iron column.
The saw strip, which he obtained from France, was 50 feet long
and 6 inches wide.   The machine was a rough smithy job, but
it worked !

Up to the 1880's the grading, or rather ' parcelling,' of lumber
for sale was a matter for the discretion and reputation of the
individual manufacturers.   The New York Lumber Auction
Company in the last century was a concern which both bought
and sold lumber on its own account, and also provided facilities
of periodical auctions for up-country lumbermen who wished
to sell their product in New York and district.   In 1886 this
concern published its private rules for the nine varieties of timber
they handled—namely, Ash, Basswood, Buttermint, Cherry,
Chestnut, Maple, Oak, Poplar, and Walnut.   Their oak rules
were as follows :

The standard lengths are 12, 14 and 16 feet.
The standard thicknesses are 1, $1\frac{1}{4}$, $1\frac{1}{2}$, 2, $2\frac{1}{2}$, 3, 4, 5 and 6 inches,
and are inspected as firsts, seconds and culls.
Firsts—Must be 8 inches and over in width, clear and free of
all defects.   Small defects allowed in accordance with the width
of board, but boards having wormholes absolutely excluded.
Seconds—at 8 inches in width one or two small knots or a little
sap may be allowed, and at 10 inches and up other small defects
may be allowed, according to width of board.
Culls—Any board that is wormy, knotty and unsound generally.

A little different from the multiple grades in the National Hardwood Lumber Association Rules to-day !   But surely the abso-
lute exclusion of wormholes is quite in accordance with modern
practice ?

During the early days of the twentieth century it can be said
that the confusion and number of private grades increased in
proportion to the vastly greater number of lumbering establishments and local associations.   Finally in 1922 Mr Herbert Hoover,

the Secretary of Commerce, offered his Department's services.
A long series of conferences between the interested parties took
place, culminating in what has passed into lumber history to-day
as the " Battle of the Thirty-second." The question involved
was as to what thickness a one-inch planed board ought to hold.
The consuming interests wanted 26/32nds, and some lumbermen
agreed, but by no means all. The contest raged so hotly that
finally Mr Secretary Hoover took time off from his multifarious
duties to hand down the " Judgment of Solomon " that it should
be 25/32nds ! By 1924 the first edition of the *American Lumber
Standards* for softwood was approved and printed, while shortly
afterwards the National Hardwood Lumber Association performed a like service for the hardwood trade. Since those days
both hardwood and softwood rules have been continually revised
and brought up to date with changing conditions.

The great developments in the Southern Pine trade took
place after the Civil War. Northern lumbermen then took a
hand in the business, and many who had come South for the
first time in their lives with the Union Armies stayed to play
their part in the reconstruction of the war-shattered countryside.
Also a number of Southerners whom the war had impoverished
saw a chance of rebuilding their fortunes by turning the cheap
and easily got pine-trees into lumber. Those who know *Gone
with the Wind* either as a novel or a film will remember that is
just what Miss Scarlett O'Hara did : she started a sawmill and
re-established her fortune. Timber-lands were cheap in those
days. Here is the evidence of Mr James D. Lacey before a
Congress Committee :

In 1880, when I first went South, in Louisiana and Mississippi,
we estimated what the value of government land was. It was
nearly all vacant then and it was timber land. In 1889 it was
offered at $1.25 an acre. We located several million acres for
Northern lumbermen. We estimated these lands would cut about
6,000 feet per acre, as they were then cutting timber. They were
not going above the first limbs ; the balance was left in the woods
or burned.

Mr A. C. Danner, penniless after four years' service in the
Confederate Army, had a fabulous career. Starting by cutting
firewood to earn his bread, he turned to hawking lumber, and

then scraped up enough capital to build a sawmill. Once started, he was soon hailed as the leading lumberman of the South, and became President of the local Bank of Mobile, an unusual honour even for an American lumberman. His own timber holdings grew to 50,000 acres, and at one time he had an agreement with the Mobile and Ohio Railroad to market all the timber from their 705,000 acres of land bordering their lines in Alabama and Mississippi. At first the lumber produced was used locally for reconstruction, but later it became necessary to reach northward for export trade. In fact, Southern Pine lumber reached the Northern States just about the time that the supplies of the fabulous white pine from around the Great Lakes were thinning out and getting more expensive to work. The Maine lumber barons began to look for new forests, if not new kingdoms, to conquer. Their logging superintendents came prospecting into the Southern forest-lands, and found much to their liking ! The terrain was level, labour was cheap, and plentiful, and finally there were billions of acres of timber-land that could be bought for 1 dollar 25 cents an acre to yield 6000 to 10,000 feet of lumber per acre. Some enormous deals were consummated : Mr William E. Dodge of New York in 1875 bought no fewer than 300,000 acres in Georgia on behalf of a syndicate. At last the banks consented to issue bonds against the security of the Southern timber-lands. It is said that the first such issue was the $560,000 First Mortgage 6 per cent. Bond Issue of the Hudson River Lumber Company of Louisiana, secured on a block of 42,390 acres of virgin timber in the parish of Calcasieu. The growing timber which secured the loan was appraised at 508,680,000 board feet, worth 1,059,780 dollars.

As will have been seen in the earlier chapters of this book, it was a combination of ice and snow, and water, that enabled the early lumbermen of North America, whether in the territory of the United States or Canada, to bring their logs to market. Without the former they could not drag the logs to the river-bank, and without the spring floods they could not float them to the cities and mills. But by the 1880's, when band-mills and their ancillary machinery were being fast introduced, mechanical plant came to the aid also of the logging crews. Mr Horace Butters, a lumberman operating in pine, is credited in 1883 with the construction of the first overhead logging cableway operated by wire rope, at Ludington, Michigan. The cableway was driven by a special double-cylinder boiler and three friction drums. The cableways were actually rigged to standing timber, like spar trees to-day, and the logs were hoisted straight out of the woods into railway-trucks. After Mr Butters' original start machinery

A " BEST " STEAM TRACTOR OF 1894 ADAPTED FROM FARM USE TO HAUL PINE LOGS ON THE McLEOD RIVER

*Photo F.*Hal Higgins Collection. *By courtesy of Ralph W. Andrews.*

companies took over the production of overhead cableways, and improvements were rapidly effected in both stability and speed of operation. Quick on the heels of the first overhead cables came the log-skidding machines for skidding logs along the ground. The Clyde Iron Works of Duluth claim to have sold the first outfit in 1903 for the City Lumber Company of Pine Bluff, Arkansas. By 1905 mechanical skidders had reached both Louisiana and the river Mississippi.

In 1893 the Best Company put its first steam-driven tractor into the forest, the forerunner of an echelon that ended by replacing the thousands of teams of oxen and horses that had done the work for over two hundred years. Their great competitors were the Holt Manufacturing Company. Two years later there were four tractors made by one or other of these Companies working in California and Oregon, near the Pacific Coast. Although these primitive steam-driven tractors trebled and quadrupled the work done by animals, they had all the same the inevitable defects of pioneering efforts. They were tall and thus top-heavy, with wheels of a large diameter. These factors bound them to operate in safety only on level ground and low gradients. The first great advance was made in 1904, when the system of tracks to obtain propulsion was invented. The first track-type steam-engine was made in the Holt works at Stockton, California. It was a 40-h.p. unit with tracks to drive it mounted at the back, and wheels in front for steering. From the time of the original invention of tracked units there has been a steady advance in design and adaptability, so that caterpillar vehicles can now operate over all types of terrain. By the way, it is said that the term ' caterpillar ' was originated by a photographer employed by the original Mr Holt to take photographs to advertise his new patent vehicle. The photographer compared the undulating action of the tracks to a caterpillar, and Mr Holt quickly seized upon the name. The Best Manufacturing Company and the Holt Manufacturing Company merged in 1925 to become the Caterpillar Tractor Company. Since then they have specialized in logging equipment for use all over the world. Before leaving the subject of log and lumber transportation reference must be made to the specialized subject of ' flumes.' These were principally used on the Pacific Coast, and their purpose was to transport manufactured lumber from the mills in the high mountains to the cities or railways in the plains. One of the earliest was made by the Madera Flume and Trading Company in the year 1875. Its length was 65 miles from the mill community in the mountains to the railway terminus at Madera. The flume had 36″ sides and was 46″ across the top, being V-shaped. Over five million board feet of lumber and 2000 kegs of nails were used in its construction. The Kings River Company in the 1890's built another flume over 62 miles long from their mills on the Kings river to Sanger. Such flumes would have a capacity of about 250,000 feet a day, the boards being bundled by iron bands into packages about 12″ square. Along the flume, men called " flume loaders " lived in huts. Their duty was to keep the structure in

repair and prevent jams in the waterway. Their food-supplies
and mail were floated to them at their lonely stations down the
flume. Inspections were periodically carried out in specially
constructed boats.

Before leaving the United States it is fitting to glance at the

'Dry-land Sailors': Flume-loaders sitting in a Hollowed Log
ready to travel down the Chute
By courtesy of Ralph W. Andrews.

lumbering industry of the West or Pacific Coast, a highly specialized area. "The West" in the language of lumbermen includes
ten states west of the Rocky Mountains—namely, Arizona, California, Colorado, Idaho, Montana, Nevada, New Mexico,
Oregon, Washington, and Wyoming.

John McLaughlin, an employee of the Hudson Bay Company,
erected the first water-driven sawmill in 1827 on the Columbia
river near Fort Vancouver. A number of other water-mills

followed, and the first steam sawmill was built by a sea-captain named James Dawson at Bodega Bay in 1843. This worthy mariner had arrived on a trading voyage to Bodega Bay two years previously, and must have been looking for somewhere to settle down. For, having secured a site suitable for a sawmill, he returned to Baltimore, where he collected a complete sawmill plant, recruited a force of millwrights, sawyers, labourers, married a wife, and triumphantly carried the whole outfit to California, where he very successfully exchanged the sea for the saw ! Other early sawmills were Joseph Gale's in Oregon, and a steam sawmill built in 1851 at the southern end of Puget Sound, in the state of Washington. It was the great Gold Rush to California in 1849 that gave a fillip to the West Coast timber trade. Much lumber was required to house the miners, and the traders who followed them. News of the vast fir forests and the easy money to be earned travelled east, and a number of the bolder lumber operators sailed round the Horn, bringing their plant and workers with them. In consequence the inlets of California and the coast farther north became dotted with sawmills driven by both water and steam.

However, the West Coast lumbering industry really got under way on a grand scale towards the close of the nineteenth century, just at the same time as the great developments in the South, and for the same basic reasons, the facts being that the apparently inexhaustible stands of white pine round the Great Lakes were at last showing signs of exhaustion, and the wealthy lumbering interests of the East were anxiously looking for fresh lands to conquer, or rather cut ! Old-established lumber families whose names had been household words in Maine and Michigan and around the Great Lakes migrated with their plant, millwrights, sawyers, and logging outfits to new sites on Puget Sound, the Columbia river, and in Washington State. A leading Pacific lumberman with a different background was Colonel Chauncey W. Griggs. The Colonel commanded a Minnesota regiment in the Civil War, and then entered the coal business in St Paul. Soon in 1887 he emigrated to Tacoma, Washington, and in company with his colleagues organized the St Paul and Tacoma Lumber Company. They built a large sawmill in Tacoma, and swiftly acquired great timberland holdings in Washington. Their work was well and truly done, and the Company continues to prosper to-day.

A Giant Redwood Tree, measuring 17½ feet across the Butt, felled on the Nego River

Photo Union Lumber Company. By courtesy of Ralph W. Andrews.

Sawmilling activities on the Coast and its immediate neighbourhood went on apace, but the difficulties of access to the
forests of the interior kept that area backward. The Rev. Henry
Spalding, a missionary to the Nez Perces Indians, built the first
interior sawmill in 1840 at Lapwai, in Idaho. It was a water-
driven sash mill, and the water-wheel was constructed of Idaho
white pine and cedar. All the work of erection was done by
the Mission Indians, who carried the sawmill plant through the
mountains by canoe and horseback from Fort Vancouver.
Another famous mill was Sutter's Mill, built at Caloma in 1847,
and the first sawmill to work pine in California. Its claim to
fame rests on the fact that the operator, Mr James W. Marshall,
discovered gold in the mill-race ! The lumbermen who came
to the West Coast had to meet difficulties of a different nature,
and on a much more gigantic scale than they had encountered
" back East." In those early days of Pacific Coast logging practically all work was manual. There were no shiny tractors, only
teams of oxen and stubborn mules. The men and their bosses
had to be tough to tackle the task at all. Such conditions endured
into the early days of the twentieth century. Now modern
invention and ingenuity put an entirely different complexion on
forest work. Here is an ' old-timer ' looking back on his
experiences with both humour and regret :

First I worked for a lumber company in the Hoh rain forest.
This was back in 1900 and in those days did we have snow ? We
had to take our shovels to our bunks with us so as to be able to
shovel our way out of the bunk house in the morning. At 4 in
the morning the iron-headed old boss would stick his mug in the
bunk house door and yell " Daylight in the swamp " and the truth
of it is it was two hours till daylight but that boss wasn't to be
argued with and out we all rolled and got on our frozen boots
and mukluks. We would all gang into the grub house at about
5 A.M. At 6 o'clock that same boss would yell " All out for the
woods." We were already five miles deep in 'em. By daylight
we would be arrived at our picnic ground and logging cedar out
of the swamp. Along about noon the cook and his crew would
show up with a flat log drawn by a horse with our pork and beans
on it and we would brush the snow off the logs and sit down to
eat in weather which was mostly around zero and I never have
known since how good pork and beans tasted and by the looks of
the pork after careful examination I sometimes wonder if the hog

A Lumberman starts his Climb to trim a Spar Tree

Note the spiked boots, and the tools hung round the waist.

Photo Leonard Frank Collection, Vancouver. By courtesy of Ralph W. Andrews.

T.—9

wasn't boiled alive as I found many a hog's hair still growing on the rind, but it tasted mighty good anyway. At 4 o'clock which was about dark in the winter the boss would yell " All in." He didn't need to tell us that as we were sure all in by that time as that boss didn't give us time to take a decent breath all day.

The Pacific Coast and the Far West carried to the eve of the First World War the picturesqueness, colour, and toughness of early logging. Well into the twentieth century logging towns had their saloons and dance-halls where the glamour-starved logger could obtain all the amusement he wanted and soon dispose of his winter's money. Here is a description by the writer Mr James Stevens in the *Four L Lumber News* of March 1927 :

> The old Humboldt, which before the Aberdeen fire, stood on the corner of Heron and South F streets, was a saloon conducted along hard-boiled but strictly honest lines by " Big Fred " Hewett. The Humboldt was a place for honest drinking and honest performing ; a logger's life was perfectly safe inside its doors. In the Humboldt no gambler could bilk him out of his hard-made earnings. No painted dancer could spill chloral in his whiskey glass. No tin-eared plug-ugly could sock him behind the ear and then frisk his pockets. If the logger himself began to yearn for battle after a few drinks he soon found himself bouncing over the sidewalk outside, with Big Fred's voice roaring behind him " Come back when you want to be decent ! I do all the fightin' for this place ! " The old-time loggers knew the Humboldt as a trusty bank. When they flooded in from the woods before the Fourth of July and Christmas the big safe often held as much as $20,000, the deposits of loggers who wanted to protect themselves from the cut-throats and harpies. Each man's money was put in a separate envelope. His name and the sum was marked down until the whole sum was gone.

The last few years have, however, changed this atmosphere to something that some may consider almost humdrum. The modern lumberman, if he is married, will live in a cosy house some distance from the operation and drive to his eight-hour-day's work in a car. If he is single and lives on the job it will be in chalets, with sheets on the bed, with shower-baths, radios, electric appliances, and all the comforts of the big city.

CHAPTER VIII

THE CANADIAN LUMBER INDUSTRY

ONE of the earliest records of Canadian forests is given by Jacques Cartier, when he voyaged along the east coast of New Brunswick in the sixteenth century. The great explorer records in his diary as follows :

> Nevertheless we went that day ashore in four places to see the goodly and sweet smelling trees that were there. We found them to be cedars, yew trees, pines, white elms, ashes, willows with many other sorts of trees to us unknown, but without any fruit.

Nicholas Denys in 1672 explored the coast from Maine to Gaspé Peninsula. He speaks of the pines as follows :

> . . . which have not the grain of the wood very coarse, but they are of forty or sixty feet in height without branches, very suitable for making planks for building both for sea and land use.

Later, travelling along the St Lawrence river, he refers to hardwoods as follows :

> . . . a great number of beautiful oaks, which would be fine for building ships, and which ought to be better than those of the northern coast, of which the wood is too soft.

The British Admiralty were the prime movers in the development of the timber trade of Lower Canada. During the great naval wars of the seventeenth and eighteenth centuries the Royal Dockyards needed a steady supply of masts and shipbuilding timbers, which were obtained from the territories bordering upon the Gulf of St Lawrence. In 1718 Messrs Hazen and White of St John had a contract to deliver " North American white pine masts, yards and bow-sprits, ash rafters, elm timber, oak timber, anchor stocks of white oak, and crooked or compass timber." The following year their Woods Surveyor reported that he had extracted one of the best yard-arms that was ever carried down the river, the length being 110 ft. and the diameter 26″. Even as early as 1722 the British Parliament passed an Act prohibiting the clearance by settlers of any white pine trees 12″

in diameter and up from the King's Woods in the colony of Canada. Apart from the Colonists, Canada's forest wealth has been devastated by fire from time immemorial. The Jesuit Father, Le Clercq, in 1677 travelled along the Miramichi, and in his diary he records a vivid picture of a typical fire :

> In order that you may understand what these burnt woods are, I will tell you that the heavens, being one day all on fire, full of tempest and thunder which rumbled and made itself heard in all parts, a thunderbolt fell at a time when the dryness was extra-ordinary, and not merely set in flames all the woods and forests which lay between Miramichis and Nipisiguit, but also burnt and consumed more than two hundred and fifty leagues of country in such a manner that nothing was to be seen except very tall and quite blackened trunks of trees.

Shipbuilding early became a stable industry in the colonies of New Brunswick and Nova Scotia. The main exports at this time were salt and dried fish, and lumber. It became customary to build the ships during the winter, load them with commodities, and sail them over to the Home Country during the summer, when, most commonly, cargo and ship were all sold together. We have knowledge that many such little ships of 200 to 300 tons burthen were built of tamarisk and spruce, but here is a statement of one Patrick Campbell, a Surveyor at the Port of St John, made in 1800, concerning ships that were entirely built of birch :

> Ships are built not only in this, but also in different bays and creeks up the river, which are of two, three or four hundred tons burden, carpenter's measurement, all of black birch. I have been on board a ship, then on the stocks, of three hundred tons, that had not a stick of any other wood in her whole hulk ; and another brig of two hundred tons, just then launched, whose cabins and state rooms were finished in the neatest manner I have ever seen, all of black birch, equal in beauty to mahogany. These vessels when fitted for sea, are loaded with lumber, and despatched to either Britain or the British West Indies. If to the former, often both ship and cargo are sold ; but if to the latter, the cargo only.

You will notice that he waxes very eloquent about the beauties of the Black Birch when used for decorating the cabins ; also the statement that it was customary to sell the ships if they went to Great Britain, but not if they went to the West Indies.

In the seventeenth and eighteenth centuries the timber of

Lower Canada passed through a number of hands before it reached its destination at an English port, or perhaps the West Indies. At the ports of New Brunswick, Quebec, and Montreal were established large financial houses, a number of them being also shipowners, importers of textiles, machinery tools, etc. Such

SHIPS WAITING TO LOAD TIMBER IN THE HARBOUR OF HALIFAX, NOVA SCOTIA, TOWARDS THE CLOSE OF THE EIGHTEENTH CENTURY

By courtesy of the Sigmund Samuel Canadiana, Royal Ontario Museum.

houses received their supplies at the ports from British merchants, who in turn made contracts with the actual lumberers. Very often the farmers along the St Lawrence waterway would turn timbermen for the winter, and, employing their labourers, horses, and oxen, would deliver the logs to contractors at the river-bank. Often in a given season 2000 animals would be thus employed.

From an earlier House of Commons Report we have the following estimate of the value of the capital investment in North American sawmills in the period 1815 to 1820 :

By a diminution of the demand from America, the capital invested in sawmills and establishments in those Colonies, stated at

150,000L. may be liable to some injury. It must be recollected, however, that the advantage given to the American Colonial trade, on which these establishments were founded, has already extended beyond the period on which those engaged in it had in mind to calculate ; and having speculated on their own views of public policy, they can have no just ground of complaint should Parliament take a different view of what that policy requires.

Very moderate, you see, in comparison with present-day astronomical figures ! But no doubt those modest Colonial sawmillers took a poor view of the findings, if the document ever reached them.

By 1835 the value of the sawmills in both Upper and Lower Canada was estimated to have reached £300,000. There were several large mills in the neighbourhood of Quebec. Messrs Gilmour and Rankin had a sawmill on the river Miramichi worth £15,000, while one belonging to a Mr Patterson was said to have cost £30,000. (It was formerly the property of Messrs Usborne, Benson, and Co.) This particular mill often worked night and day during the short open season, when it would produce 3000 12 ft. planks every twenty-four hours. Its owner was said to have loaded thirty or forty ships a year during the Napoleonic Wars, when Baltic timber was not to be had. These mills were, of course, water-driven, and the provision of the extensive dams necessary to hold up the water-supply was often the most expensive part of the project. They employed gang saws with three or four blades, and the standard thickness was $3\frac{1}{4}''$. The machinery is said to have included circular saws " for the purpose of cutting the ends and cutting off where there is a wane-edge." If this were true of circular saws it is a very early mention of their employment !

Such was the effect of the crippling of the Baltic timber trade by the Napoleonic Wars that, by their cessation in 1815, the production of timber formed almost the whole commerce of New Brunswick. About one-quarter of the population was engaged or interested in the production of wood. During the Wars the Government of the day had laid heavy duties on foreign wood, and admitted the Canadian imports duty-free. At the conclusion of peace in 1815 a considerable agitation took place in trade circles to have the duties equalized. A Committee of the House of Commons was set up to consider the matter,

Woodsmen felling Pine-trees in Upper Canada (1842)
Author's collection.

and a war of pamphlets started. So high was the feeling in New Brunswick that when the news of the defeat of some proposals to place duties upon Canadian timber was received it was said that it was celebrated with public rejoicings, as much as if an enemy had been defeated ; illuminations took place, and oxen were roasted entire in the streets of Halifax and St John !

A number of Select Committees of both the Houses of Parliament took evidence *inter alia* of the organization and habits of the lumbering fraternity. In many cases, as mentioned previously, farmers turned lumbermen for the winter only. But there was a class of professional lumbermen and raftsmen who contracted with the big merchants from year to year to fell and handle their timber in return for advances of cash and supplies in the form of a ' grub stake.' Such men were recruited from the towns on the St Lawrence and Miramichi, and even from Maine and Vermont. Unfortunately some of these men had a reputation for fecklessness and for breaking their bargains. These lumbering and felling gangs usually numbered forty or fifty men under the leadership of an individual known as a master-lumberer, although groups of eighty workers were organized for large operations. These lumbering gangs went up-country in August and September with their stores to establish their camps and work the winter through. They would not return to the towns and ports until the following April or May, when, with luck and a good flow of water in the rivers, their logs would have come out.

The Scottish firm Pollock, Gilmour, and Co., of Glasgow, were large operators, with their principal mill at Miramichi and other establishments at St John, Quebec, and Montreal. They imported annually into the Canadas £100,000 worth of linens, cottons, and hardware, bringing out an equivalent value in timber. As an example of the size of their operations in the year 1834, they dispatched to the various ports of the United Kingdom over three hundred ships, some for their own account and the remainder against forward contracts to a number of regular British importers. These vessels averaged about 200 standards a cargo, and it is noteworthy that they were considered large ships for those days. The shipments consisted of birch, pine, and spruce, the last predominating. This firm was stated to have employed in their operations annually, either directly or indirectly, over 5000 men and 2000 horses and oxen.

The following quotation, from Mr Allan Gilmour, is of interest as giving a comparison between the value of softwoods in 1835, not only at the various Canadian ports, but also including Memel, from the Baltic :

Prices of timber, 1835, at the undermentioned shipping ports, free on board, per load of 50 cubic feet.

	per load.
	£ s. d.
Memel crown timber	1.14.0
seconds timber..	1. 7.0
Quebec red pine timber £1.13.2d., from which a duty is paid to the Crown of 4s. 2d., leaving	1. 9.0
yellow pine ditto	17.0
St John ⎫ Miramichi, and ⎬ ditto .. .. Chaleur Bay ⎭	1. 3.0
St John spruce deals	1. 8.2

Mr Henry Warburton, M.P., the London yard-keeper mentioned as giving evidence in 1835, said that large prime timber from the Canadas was exceedingly valuable, and, on being asked if it required large ships to bring it, he replied as follows :

Certainly, but more especially a large raft-port at the head and stern of the vessel, through which the logs can pass, when the ship is loading and discharging its cargo. If a ship of moderate size is so constructed as to have large raft-ports, she will be able to bring very large logs of timber. It is the large yellow pine timber from Miramichi, which more than any other is applicable to those superior purposes before described. It has been usual of late years to assort a cargo from Miramichi, on its being discharged from the ship and rafted, into timber of three qualities ; that which is both large and clean (large meaning above 18 inches square), that which is small and clean, and that which is knotty and coarse. The first kind, which consists of the large butts of trees, often from 22 to 24 inches square, and clear of knots, is what is consumed by musical-instrument makers, and will sell for say 80s. a load. It also is the material out of which they cut with a machine scale-boards, as they are called, i.e. the thin board from which hat-boxes are made. The small clean timber will answer for a variety of purposes, in which wood free from knots is required, as for the laths of Venetian blinds, etc., this will sell for 70s. The coarse is used by the builder, and will sell for about 55s. They are large ships in general, however, that bring cargoes of this description, ships of 350 tons and upwards to 500 tons.

The worthy yard-keeper and his father before him had been successfully operating a London retail timber business from 1757. His account is extremely valuable, not only as giving a first-hand account of the grading of the Miramichi Yellow Pine timbers, but also as describing the use to which the various grades were put in the spacious days of the Regency. It is noteworthy that the musical-instrument makers, the craftsmen of spinets and harpsichords (forerunners of the early piano), took the first choice. The builders came last, but who would not eulogize even over their quality to-day ? No doubt this Miramichi Yellow Pine still stands as good as new in many a surviving Regency house in both London and the Provinces.

As mentioned previously, Quebec became the entrepôt for the lumber trade of the wide St Lawrence and its many tributaries. In fact, by 1825 the French-Canadian city had become the greatest timber port the world had ever known, and—such is the irony of history—mainly through her British connexions. Timber was floated down to Quebec from the many small rivers that ran into the St Lawrence, commencing at thirty leagues below the town, and reaching up to above Montreal. Much wood was also obtained from the Bay of Quinte, and, last but by no means least, the Ottawa river made a large contribution. Quebec not only loaded out the wood, but her dockyards built wooden ships to carry home the St Lawrence timbers. In 1852 it is recorded that there were twenty-five shipbuilding yards in the port, and in 1855 fifty ships were launched in one season ; while in 1825 was built the largest wooden ship the world had seen to date, the *Baron of Renfrew*, with a lading of 5888 tons. In the table at p. 141 is given a list and valuation of some of the principal lumber establishments and shipyards at Quebec in the year 1835. It will be noticed from the table that a number of the lumber establishments were situated on Sillery Cove, just above the port. Here a number of merchants had offices, from which they could supervise the breaking up of the great rafts and the dispersal of the logs into sorting-booms. It was said that in the late spring the waterfront looked like a vast logging camp, while the water was black with logs. Here also the logs were graded

TIMBER RAFTS AT THE JUNCTION OF THE OTTAWA AND ST LAWRENCE RIVERS (1841)
Author's collection.

for shipment and redressed where necessary.   Among other leading merchants it will be seen that Gilmour and Co. had large premises at Wolfe's Cove.   This was the famous cove at which General Wolfe landed his troops at dead of night to steal up the cliffs and next morning fight the famous battle which gained Quebec for the British in the year 1759, losing his life at the moment of victory.   These premises were valued at £20,000 and gave employment to 150 men.   Here were the great ponds formed by chained booms for sorting the logs as the rafts were broken up.   The solid stone piers jutting 150 ft. out into the river, behind which the rafts were brought to rest after their long voyage down the St Lawrence, can still be located to-day by their solid foundations, over 20 ft. wide at the base.   Ashore were spacious store-sheds in which were stored the supplies for the lumberers in their winter logging campaigns ; also workshops for repairing gear and tackle, together with everything necessary for fitting out ships for the long voyage across the Atlantic : there were no five-day passages in those days ! Last but not least was the lumber-yard for supplying Quebec and district with sawn deals.

Other notable names in the list are W. Sharples and Son at Sillery Cove and W. Price and Co. at New Liverpool, with a lumber establishment valued at £10,000.   It will be noticed that these lumbering establishments were all situate outside the city, as they needed extensive waterfronts and a considerable area of backland.   The ordinary merchanting business was conducted at the deep-water wharves off the Lower Town.   It is alleged that the big merchant houses at Quebec made the big money that was undoubtedly made in the pine trade of those days.   Those wonderful Yellow Pine logs were delivered at Quebec by the master-lumberers for an average of 1s. per ft. cube, and these worthy men appeared from contemporary records to be more often in the debt of their merchant backers than to have a worthwhile credit at the end of the season's work.

We are told that the principal part of the timber was taken from Crown land, and that the Crown allowed the liberty to fell it on certain tracts at a merely nominal rate.   It appears that this rate was fixed with the main object of preventing the lumbering gangs from fighting with one another over their alleged rights.   Before the Government took a hand and fixed nominal

List and Valuation of Some of the Principal Lumber Establishments and Shippards in Quebec in 1835

NAME OR PLACE	DESCRIPTION	VALUE £	PROPRIETOR	BY WHOM OCCUPIED	NUMBER OF MEN EMPLOYED
Cap Rouge	Lumber establishment	3,000	J. Duchesnay	Atkinson, Usborne, & Co.	40
New London Cove	,, ,,	1,000	Munro	M. B. Farlin	15
Sillery Cove	,, ,,	3,000	The King	M. B. Farlin	40
,, ,,	,, ,,	2,000	,, ,,	W. Sharples & Son	30
,, ,,	,, ,,	2,500	,, ,,	Pemberton Bros.	35
St Michael's Cove	,, ,,	10,000	Ursuline Nuns	C. Wood & Gray	65
Woodfield Harbour	,, ,,	5,000	W. Sheppard	Sheppard & Campbell	35
Usborne's Cove	,, ,,	6,000	G. Usborne	Atkinson, Usborne, & Co.	40
Wolfe's Cove	,, ,,	20,000	A. Gilmour & Co.	A. Gilmour & Co.	150
Black's Cove	Ship-building & lumber-yard	5,000	Campbell & Black	George Black	150
Munn's	,, ,,	5,000	Munn	J. & J. Jeffrey	20
River St Charles	Lumber establishment	2,000	H. Gowen	H. Gowen & Co.	30
Goudie's	Ship-building & lumber-yard	4,000	H. J. Caldwell	Sundry Persons	100
Point Levi	Patent slip	2,000	George Taylor	G. Taylor & Son	30
St Charles Cove	Lumber establishment	1,500	Sampson	Jones, Murray, & Co.	10
Patton's Cove	,, ,,	2,000	W. Patton & Co.	W. Patton & Co.	40
Hadlow Cove	,, ,,	2,500	,, ,,	W. Price & Co.	20
New Liverpool	,, ,,	10,000	W. Price & Co.	W. Price & Co.	60

rates the lumberers used to go about as freebooters, taking what timber they fancied and bearing down all opposition by force. Nevertheless the wages paid by the master-lumbermen were high for those days, and attracted the strong young Canadians from the more humdrum farm life. Experienced lumberers received from ten to twelve dollars a month, whereas agricultural labourers and farm servants were paid monthly at the rate of five to six dollars. Also many immigrants who had received grants of land in Lower Canada of fifty to a hundred acres found they could not clear their land fast enough to support their families, and these men were accustomed to go lumbering in the winter for the sake of ready cash.

Many of the gangs went far up-country, always in reach of a river, and were accustomed to spend the hard winter months in the roughest 'shacks,' as the crude dormitories were colloquially named. These huts were constructed of rough-hewn logs, caulked with moss to keep out the worst of the weather, and often with only a hole in the roof to let out the smoke from the central hearth. The rough bunks were constructed round the walls, so that all the occupants had a fair share in the log fire, which was kept going night and day.

The coming of the railways made a great difference to the operations of the lumberers and their backers, the great merchants of Quebec. Previously it had not been possible to handle the timber, however fine, which grew more than five miles from a river or waterway, such as a connecting lake. Five miles was the maximum distance which horses or oxen could haul the great sleighs over the specially prepared iced roads. Cases are on record where a team of horses would haul a hundred tons of logs on one sleigh. Ingenious, if crude, brakes were used on these enormous loads. Before the nineteenth century was out the need for forest conservation became apparent, and as early as 1885 a Forestry Department within the Department of the Interior was established. This body recommended the setting up of forestry schools in Quebec and Ontario, and later an Inspector of Forests was appointed and a Forest Service created. One of the Government's directions to the new branch was :

To inspect the existing timber reserves, to visit timbered lands generally, with a view to setting apart further reserves and to look into the causes of forest destruction, particularly by fire, and to suggest means of protection.

A great step forward took place in 1906, when the Dominion Government convened the first Convention on Forestry at Ottawa. A result of this Convention was the enactment of the Forest Reserves Act, setting apart 5390 square miles under a Superintendent of Forestry, to become in 1930 the Dominion Forest Service. Fire has always been the chief enemy of Canada's forests, but it was not until 1870 in Quebec and 1878 in Ontario that legislation was enacted. Under these early laws the forest concessionnaire co-operated with the Government in providing a fire-fighting service on the basis of a fifty-fifty sharing of the expenses. By 1905, however, the Government took over the whole service themselves, employing at the outset no fewer than four hundred fire rangers to supervise the forests. The number of officers has by now, of course, greatly increased.

It is recorded that Philemon Wright, a citizen of the United States from Vermont, New England, crossed the border, settled on a Canadian farm, and, turning lumberman, first logged on the river Ottawa in 1807. He was no doubt encouraged to this pioneer effort by the acute shortage of timber in Great Britain, brought about by Napoleon's Continental blockade. As the business of ' driving ' the river became organized, great rafts were put together in the upper reaches containing up to 100,000 ft. cube. Huts were built on the rafts to accommodate the crews, which might amount to fifty men. They would work the rafts down the slow reaches of the river with great sweeps, while simple sails would be hoisted when the wind was favourable. The Ottawa river changes from a placid-flowing stream to a roaring rapid at frequent points on its course. When this occurred the full efforts of the crew were needed to meet the quickly changing situation. Over the slower rapids the complete raft would slide like an undulating snake without much trouble. Before shooting the fast rapids the great rafts would be broken up into their component sections, which consisted always of 26-ft. ' cribs.' The reason for this consistent size will appear later. After the rapid had been safely passed the component ' cribs ' would be assembled together in some quiet backwater and once more lashed together into the great raft, which formed the dwelling-place of its crew for three or four weeks, the time it took to make the journey into the St Lawrence and down to the boom at Quebec.

Besides the difficulties of the rapids, there were narrow gorges obstructed by rocks, and at places on the long journey the rafts would have to be transferred from the river to lake and *vice*

FRENCH-CANADIAN RIVERMEN FLOATING LOGS ON THE LAKE OF THE
TWO MOUNTAINS, QUEBEC
Mid-nineteenth century.
Author's collection.

versa. Both the gorges and the transfer from one water-level to another were circumvented by the same method of constructing sloping ' slides ' by cutting through the rocky banks. These ' slides ' were maintained by Government, and each was in the charge of a Slide Superintendent, who, besides keeping the water-chute clear, collected the toll of 25 cents a ' crib,' which made the structures self-supporting. Now, all these ' slides ' were constructed to a standard width of 26½ ft., and that is the reason why in their turn all the component ' cribs ' of the great rafts were made 26 ft. in length. In later years an association of logging companies took over the ' slides ' from Government and

undertook their maintenance and service. The rivermen were
organized into 'Brigades,' each under its own leader. The Ottawa
River ' Brigades ' were mainly composed of Scotsmen, while the
rivermen of the Gatineau river were mainly French-Canadians.
When the respective ' drives' inevitably met at the junction

A TIMBER RAFT NEGOTIATING THE TIMBER SLIDE ON THE OTTAWA
RIVER (1840)

Author's collection.

of the two rivers below Bytown, later Ottawa, terrific fights
would take place between the rival gangs, and bitter feuds would
be carried over from season to season.

The story of the pine trade on the Ottawa river may well
be studied through the history of the famous firm of Gillies
Bros., of Braeside, Ontario. James Gillies, the first of that ilk,
landed in Quebec with his wife and five children in 1821, to
settle up-country at the township of Lanark. It was, however,
his son John who really put the family into the lumber business.
Starting in 1832, he took up numerous forest concessions and
built the original mill on the river Clyde. It is said that this

sawmill had one wooden frame with a single upright saw weigh-ing 90 lb., which John carried on his own back fifty-five miles over the primitive roads from Brockville to Lanark. He actually started sawing in the year 1842, and sold pine boards at six to eight dollars per 1000 feet. As his operations extended, as well as

TIMBER SLIDE AT LES CHATS, UPPER CANADA (1841)
Author's collection.

sawing for the local market, John Gillies was accustomed to ship lumber down the Rideau Canal, and also to supply rafts of squared timbers for the English market. In 1862 John, son of the founder, purchased 300,000 square miles of forests known as the Milmore limits. At the same time he bought sawmills at Carleton Place to saw the logs from the new holdings. There had been a small settlement and sawmill at Braeside since 1822, and it was in 1872 that the Gillies family purchased the Braeside mill, lumber-yards, and considerable areas of land which now form the Headquarters of the Company. This mill at Braeside was entirely rebuilt in 1893 so as to house a twin circular saw for primary conversion, a 52-in. Wickes gang saw, two band-saws, and two resaws with modern edgers and trimmers. By

1909 these same mills were cutting from 30 to 35 million board feet of lumber in the season. This mill ran successfully all through World War I, only to be completely destroyed by fire with all its plant in January 1919. By April 1921, however, an entirely new mill building, completely equipped with plant to give a daily output of 200,000 board feet, and electrically driven, was in full operation once more. In 1927 a planing mill was added, with modern rapid-feed resaws, stackers, and planers, thus providing for the production of dressed as well as rough lumber. With certain alterations to layout, and additions of the most modern plant, this is the mill that is running to-day.

In the early Colonial days the Admiralty in London appointed Royal Naval Contractors to supply them with the pine masts and shipbuilding timbers required for the Royal Dockyards in Great Britain. The obligation on these contractors was to deliver their timber at the dockyards. This method of trading encouraged the development of middlemen, who were accustomed to sail to the St Lawrence and themselves contract for the wood with the settler, who would do the rough-hewing and squaring and also haul the timber during the hard winter months. However, in 1826 this system was changed, and the Canadian Government commenced to issue licences to cut timber on Crown land. We are told that at first there was some considerable abuse by reason of large tracts of forest-land granted to speculators who had no intention of working the timber themselves, but merely intended to hold their territories for the inevitable rise. In 1841 the outcry against these practices forced the Government to tighten up their regulations, and lay down definite specifications, with sworn measurers to do the supervision.

A number of canal routes were opened during the years 1820 to 1840, and in consequence the wood from Eastern Canada commenced to flow into the United States market ; notably a quantity of excellent oak was tapped by means of the Rideau Canal, which was constructed under the supervision of Colonel Bye, of the Royal Engineers, as a precautionary measure following the War of 1812. Arising out of the Napoleonic Wars, very considerable preferences had been given by the British Government to the Canadian market. Over the years these preferences on Colonial timber were gradually lowered, until with Sir Robert Peel in office they were reduced so drastically in 1845 to 1846 as to leave them quite nominal, to be finally swept away in 1866. The effect of these fiscal changes was to introduce uncertainty into the Canadian pine market. The signing of the Reciprocity Treaty with the United States in 1854

KING EDWARD VII, WHEN PRINCE OF WALES, RIDING A TIMBER RAFT ON THE RIDEAU TIMBER SLIDE, IN COMPANY WITH CANADIAN OFFICIALS

" *Illustrated London News,*" *October 20, 1860.*

was therefore a considerable relief to the lumber operators. Under its terms both countries granted free entry to the other of many forest products, including sawn timber boards and scantlings, but not planed material. The actual effect of this treaty was a marked increase in exports from Eastern Canada to the United States. In fact, during the next three years, for the first time in Canadian history, exports to the United States exceeded those to Great Britain.

The thrusting forward of the great trans-continental railways also gave a fillip to the wood trade. On the setting up of the United Province of Canada, Queen Victoria in 1858 selected Ottawa as the new capital. Up to that time Ottawa had been a small township named Bytown, after the worthy Colonel. The consequent boom in land and building created great activity in the lumber industry of both Quebec and Ontario. The United States Civil War in 1861 at first dislocated the lumber business owing to the falling off of trade with both the United States and Great Britain. With the cessation of war and the reconstruction period, the demand for Canadian timber soared again to greater heights than ever. By the year 1866 the Canadian Government became concerned over the denuding of Canadian forest wealth by shipments to the United States, much of the profit obviously going to American sources. For this and other reasons the Reciprocity Treaty was terminated in 1866, and both countries erected tariff walls. The United States put a duty of 20 per cent. on Canadian imports, while in their turn the Canadians levied an export duty of one dollar per 1000 feet on round pine logs, with the dual purpose of reviving the trade in squared timbers and encouraging the sawing and planing of lumber in the Canadian mills. The Franco-Prussian War brought a large demand for lumber from Europe. It is recorded that by 1874 the annual production in the Ottawa Valley had reached 25 million cubic feet of squared timber, and not less than 400 million board feet of sawn lumber. The Franco-Prussian War was followed by a period of depression, but in 1878 Sir John MacDonald was carried into power in the Dominion Election on his new national policy of tariff walls and trade protection. The carrying out of this policy stimulated both Canadian trade and industry, and was joined with the tremendous undertaking of the building of the trans-continental railways. In consequence the Canadian lumber trade now entered the decade of its greatest growth.

The pine trade increased largely in the boom that followed the First World War. Unfortunately the wonderful width which at the turn of the century had brought the name of ' Broad pine ' could no longer be supplied, as the virgin forests were cut over, but all the same production figures mounted. By 1932, however, the world's greatest slump reached Canada. Many mills were temporarily closed down, and in the years

1932 to 1933 very few companies carried out any logging operations. The value of lumber on the pine market fell to approximately half the cost of production. By 1935, however, largely assisted by the Imperial Preference negotiated at Ottawa, the pine trade was on the move again, and production figures once more reached their old level. During the War shipments of pine, largely in the better grades, continued to reach the United Kingdom, and were used principally for pattern-making and other high-class purposes. Following the War, and in particular during the last few years, there has been a strong demand for pine in Canada itself. Fostered by the principal mills and under the auspices of the White Pine Bureau of the Canadian Lumbermen's Association, its uses have been much extended, so that the wood now furnishes a considerable contribution to the building boom which is now taking place in that country.

It may be said that the great explorer Captain Cook discovered the forests of British Columbia. In the course of his voyage of exploration he refitted his ships *The Resolution* and *Discovery* with masts and timber taken from the forests of Vancouver. One of the next arrivals on the coast of British Columbia was Captain Vancouver, after whom Vancouver was named. During the closing years of the eighteenth century it was customary for ships' captains to visit Vancouver Island and its neighbourhood to fill their holds with timber and masts, to be carried to China and the ports of the South Pacific. Both the timber and spars would, of course, be merely rough-hewn. The British Admiralty were also anxious to obtain masts and spars for their Pacific stations. In this connexion it is related that in 1849 one Captain Brotchie sailed from London with the ship *Albion*. He carried a licence to cut spars for the Admiralty on Vancouver Island and surrounding territories. Very soon the gallant captain had loaded his ship with no fewer than 42 spars 60 ft. to 100 ft. in length, ranging up to 26 in. square. At this time both Canada and the United States were stretching out their fingers westward, and the boundary between the two countries had yet to be defined. Unfortunately, just as Captain Brotchie was about to leave with his cargo, an American Navy cutter seized his ship and imprisoned its crew on a charge of illegal timber felling. Many years later the affair was settled by the British Ambassador in Washington, but long before that the ship and its cargo had been sold locally to clear expenses.

Undeterred by the loss of his good ship, Captain Brotchie set up an establishment near Fort Rupert, at the northern end of Vancouver Island, and there commenced to cut timber for spars. He actually trained the local Indians to do the labour of felling and hewing the immense timbers. Unfortunately for him, the Lords Commissioners of the Admiralty in London had by now lost all interest in his doings, and his project was abandoned.

To cast back a little in time, it was on a bright April day in 1825 that the three-masted sailing-vessel *William and Anne* entered the mouth of the Columbia river carrying among its passengers the famous botanist David Douglas, whose name has been carried down to posterity in that great timber tree the Douglas Fir. It is of interest that Douglas did not actually discover the fir named after him ; it was, in fact, already known to science as *Pinus taxifolia*. We are told, however, that the immense size of these trees quite amazed him. He measured some of the fallen giants from the virgin forests around him, and found the largest to be 227 ft. long and 48 ft. in circumference. In order to obtain some of the cones for his sponsors, the Royal Horticultural Society of London, he was reduced to bombarding the tops of these standing giants with buck-shot. The tree, however, which Douglas actually did discover and named for the first time was the sugar-pine (*Pinus lambertiana Dougl.*), which previous to his visit had not been known to Europeans.

Among other trees that were either found or first introduced by Douglas were the following : Sitka Spruce, which he named *Pinus menziesii*, in honour of the explorer, but which, of course, is now known as *Picea sitchensis* ; Western White Pine, which he first found in the vicinity of Mount St Helena, and to which he gave its present name of *Pinus monticola* ; and the Monterey Pine (*Pinus radiata Don* ; *Pinus insignis Douglas*). Douglas in his diary records a number of exciting and curious adventures, but probably one of the most fantastic is the story that, in 1826, on his return to England, he washed out enough grains of gold from the clotted earth on the roots of his specimens to make himself a watch-seal ; apparently, although a botanist and not a metallurgist, he had, in fact, anticipated the discovery of gold on the Pacific Coast by over twenty years, its official date of discovery being 1848.

It is recorded that the first sawmill in British Columbia was built in 1846 at Parsons Bridge, near Victoria, on Vancouver Island. Following the famous Gold Rush to the Fraser river in 1858, a number of small mills were built to supply the wants of the miners in the shape of shanties and rough furniture. It is an interesting fact that sea-captains, usually in retirement, were accustomed to use the knowledge obtained on their voyages and take posts in the timber trade, and this particularly applies to a Captain Stamp, who in 1861 was appointed the first manager of the large sawmill erected at Port Alberni by a London firm of the name of Anderson and Anderson. In fact, the mill was named Stamp's Mill, after the renowned captain. This mill the following year exported lumber and spars to the value of over 100,000 dollars, whereas it is interesting that two years before in 1859 the Colony of British Columbia imported over 3 million feet from San Francisco. In 1864 the first timber lease was granted on Vancouver Island, and in that year the first complete cargo was loaded for Australia in the s.s. *Ellen Lewis*. By the year 1867 over a dozen large mills were operating on Vancouver Island and the mainland.

The history of a typical British Columbia sawmill is that of the Chemainus plant now owned by MacMillan and Bloedel, first started in 1862 by Thomas G. Askew in the form of a small water-powered mill, operating a primitive vertical saw, costing 3000 dollars and cutting some 2000 feet of lumber per day. The first circular saws were installed in 1885, when Mrs Askew, the widow, sold the plant to Croft and Severne. This increased the capacity to 15,000 feet. By the end of the century still more plant had been installed, and capacity had been increased to 60,000 feet per day. In 1944, still on the same site, Mr E. P. Taylor bought the property, and at this time the equipment consisted of three main bandsaws with ancillary trimmers, edgers, and gang resaws, 15 drying kilns, and a thousand-foot loading wharf for ocean-going ships. By this time the annual output had risen to 80 million board feet. In 1946 the property was purchased by the H. R. MacMillan Export Company, Ltd, and under their able management has undergone further phenomenal development.

The period down to the end of the nineteenth century was one of continued expansion. An outstanding date was 1866, when the Canadian Pacific Railway reached the coast, marking the beginning of the railway business and its consequent increase in the development of the Colony. By 1891 fifty-seven principal sawmills were in operation, together with many small portable mills. The total cut that year was over 88 million board feet. At the end of the century this figure had risen to well over 200 million board feet, giving a total revenue to the Government from the British Columbia lumber industry of approximately 116,000 dollars. To those who know the magnificent forestry service of British Columbia it is interesting to note that the first forest was inspected in the year 1888, and at the same time Government records of production were first published. In 1910, as the result of the Royal Commission on timber and forestry, the British Columbia Forestry Service was permanently established.

The year 1914 saw the opening of the Panama Canal, with its immense influence on the trade of British Columbia in general and the lumber industry in particular. By that date the value of lumber production in the Colony was estimated at close upon 20 million dollars. The First World War brought considerable difficulties to the lumber industry, mainly due to the lack of shipping. This was partly compensated by the fact of the large increase in demand from the prairie provinces, owing to the prosperity of agriculture. In fact, in 1918 consignments inland amounted to three times the value of the pre-war goods. In spite of shipping difficulties the quantity of aeroplane spruce (which had a very high priority) shipped to the United Kingdom during the War amounted to no less than 35 million board feet. The British Columbia lumber industry are very fond of referring to their " Banner Years," and the first of these occurred in 1920, when all previous records for production, the value of forest output, and forest revenues, together with exports overseas, were beaten. A second Banner Year occurred in 1929, when again all the records already established were broken.

In view of the great interest now taken in forest reserves and management licences, it is interesting to record that the Department of Lands in 1921 established the first reserve of 1500 acres in the Okanagan Areas. By 1927 the production of sawn lumber was estimated to be well over 2000 million board feet, while the Government revenue derived from forest products reached over 4 million dollars. By 1932 the 'great slump' struck the British Columbia lumber industry with full force. Both production and prices fell steeply. However, in the same year the Ottawa Agreement was signed, establishing a 10-per-cent. preference on Canadian lumber shipped to the United Kingdom. Next year a delegation from the British Columbia lumber industry visited the United Kingdom for the first time, and every possible effort was made to establish a market in the Home Country. To such good effect was this done that in 1933 British Columbia lumber exports to the United Kingdom reached 271 million board feet.

Soon after, a Trade Treaty between Canada and the United States was signed reducing the duty on British Columbia lumber to 2 dollars per 1000 feet, and establishing a quota for Douglas Fir and Hemlock. To show the great progress made by the British Columbia lumber industry, it should be recorded that the Colony's share of the total export of timber from the whole of the Pacific Coast to Australia rose from 16 per cent. in 1929 to no less than 92 per cent. in 1934 ; to China from 11 per cent. to 24 per cent. ; and in the case of the United Kingdom there was a substantial rise from 23 per cent. to 80 per cent. By the outbreak of the Second World War British Columbia's total lumber exports had reached a figure of over 1000 million board feet, of which no fewer than 600 million board feet were shipped to the United Kingdom. During the War, in spite of shipping difficulties, large quantities of British Columbia lumber continued to reach the United Kingdom, and, indeed, formed the greater part of the softwood stock available for the war effort.

CHAPTER IX

THE SPANISH MAIN AND MAHOGANY

MAHOGANY was first brought to Europe, like tobacco, from the Spanish Main, in the ships of explorers and sea-rovers. Cortes' Chronicler says the Conqueror of Mexico first saw the natives of Santo Domingo (Hispaniola) using the wood to make their crude canoes. Realizing its value, he ordered a number of small sailing-craft and pinnaces to be constructed for his fleet. St Pierre's *Studies of Nature*, published at the end of the eighteenth century, tells us that in the Antilles is found the mahogany which is called cedar, because of its incorruptibility. The tree is so large, it is related, that from the trunk of a single tree is made a boat to carry forty persons. One of the earliest shipments of mahogany to arrive in Spain was naturally presented to the King ! Fascinated by its bright colour, Philip II ordered it to be employed for the doors, windows, bookshelves, and desks of the library of the great Escorial Palace commenced in 1584. This is the first-known use of mahogany in Europe.

The earliest piece of wood, however, that bears the marks of European craftsmanship dates back to 1514, sixteen years after the discovery of America by Christopher Columbus. In the Treasury of the Cathedral at Santo Domingo to-day is a rough mahogany cross bearing the date 1514. The cross bears an inscription stating that it was employed to mark upon the ground the centre of the building. The Cathedral itself, completed in 1540, contains much finely carved mahogany. Another fine example of early Colonial Spanish work is the choir-stalls from the cathedral at Lima, Peru. These stalls date from the middle of the seventeenth century, and have been acquired by the Hispanic Society of New York. John Evelyn has the honour of being the first writer to mention mahogany in English literature. In his *Sylva* (second edition) is recorded : " There are many kinds of wood in the Western Indies besides Acajou that breed no worms." It is curious that he uses the French term " Acajou," and not the Spanish or English equivalent. The word mahogany

MAHOGANY CHOIR-STALLS FROM THE
CATHEDRAL AT LIMA, PERU

By courtesy of the Mahogany Association, Inc.

is of uncertain origin. It would probably be a fair guess to say that it is derived from a Caribbean native word, but this cannot be confirmed. Mahogany under the guise " Mothogoney " first appears in English literature in 1671 in the book *America*, by John Ogilby. Linnæus, the great botanist, turned the word into Latin in 1761 as " Mahogani." The large number of variants found in the old records is remarkable even for the loose spelling of those days. The writer has found the following, and there may well be others : mahogany, mohogeny, muhaganees, mohogany, mothogeney, mahogena, mahogon. The New World species of mahogany was given its botanical name *Mahogani Swietenia*, after Baron von Swieten (1700-72), the famous physician to Maria Theresa, Empress of Austria. One of the earliest Englishmen to set eyes on the mahogany-tree was Sir Walter Raleigh. In 1597 he caused it to be used for the repair of his ships on the celebrated voyage to the West Indies. Captain Dampier, the famous sea-captain and buccaneer, has the following to say in 1681 concerning mahogany, or, as it was sometimes originally named by the Spaniards, who were not certain of its botanical identity, cedrela or cedar:

> It was concluded to go with all our ships to St Andreas, near the Isle of Providence, and besides at this Island, we might build canoes, it being plentifully stored with large Cedars, and for this reason, the Jamaica men come hither frequently to build—Cedar being very fit for building. We reckon the pereagos and canoes, which are built of cedar, the best of any.

It has been recorded in Lunan's *Hortus Jamaicensis* that in 1724 a Dr Gibbons of London procured some mahogany from his brother, who was a sea-captain. He caused a cabinet-maker named Wollaston to make it into a box to hold candles. It happened that the Duchess of Buckingham saw the box, and much admired its rosy colour and fine polish. The Duchess was not satisfied until she had begged some of the new wood to make a bureau for herself, thus starting the fashion in Court circles. Earlier than that Celia Fiennes, a much travelled lady, writing in her diary in the years 1692–95, says :

> Trinity Colledge Chapple which was not finished the last tyme I was at Oxford, but now is a beautifull magnificent Structure, its lofty and curiously painted the rooffe and sides the history of Christ's ascension and very fine Carving of thin white wood just like that at Windsor, it being the same hand [Grinling Gibbons] the whole Chappel is wanscoated with Walnut-tree and the fine sweet wood, the same which that the Lord Orfford brought over when High Admiral of England and has wanscoated his hall and staircase with, it is sweet like Cedar and of a reddish coullour, but the graine much finer and well vein'd.

The overmantel of the altar still stands, and has been identified as Havana Cedar. Further on her travels, Celia Fiennes, fortunately for us a most inquisitive young lady, writes :

> Admiral Russells, who is now Lord Orford . . . it stands 3 mile from New Market. The hall is very noble paved with freestone a square of black marble . . . it's wanscoated with Wallnutt tree the pannells and rims round with Mulberry tree that is a lemon coullour and the moldings beyond it round are of a sweete outlandish wood not much differing from Cedar but of a finer graine ; the chaires are all the same.

Thus mahogany, or cedrela, as it was still called, had appeared as a rare, choice wood in England before the close of the seventeenth century. In fact, the stage was all set for the refined and beautiful craftsmanship of the eighteenth-century cabinet-makers. This period has been rightly called " The Golden Age of Mahogany." The earliest record of the wood in English royal circles was in 1724, when the following entry is found in the Royal Bill Books, from the reign of George I :

2 Mohogony Desart tables upon brass wheels £31.10.0

| 2 Mohogony Clothes Chests | .. | .. | .. | .. | £16. 0.0 |
| A Mohogony Supping Table | .. | .. | .. | .. | £4. 0.0 |

In the decade 1730–40 was built Houghton Hall, the seat of the Prime Minister, Robert Walpole. The architect, Mr Kent, is said to have used whole cargoes of mahogany for panelling the rooms and making staircases, doors, window-frames, etc. The house was large, furnished in walnut and mahogany in the delightful new style, for it was in 1754 that Thomas Chippendale published *The Gentleman and Cabinet Maker's Director.*

We are indebted to Mr R. W. Symons for his researches in the Public Record Office and other files. He tells us that the first reference to mahogany in the statistics of the imports which are filed at the Public Record Office is under the date of Christmas 1699–Christmas 1700, as follows :

> Jamaica.
> Wood Mohogony, 36 pcs. = £5.

Also under date of Christmas 1709–Christmas 1710 :

> Jamaica.
> Wood voc. Muhaganees 96 Foot £2.8.

While from the *London Gazette* of February 22 to 25, 1702, he has garnered the following :

> By the Principal Commissioners for Prizes. On Wednesday the 3rd of March next, at 9 in the morning, will be exposed to publick Sale by the Candle, London, a Parcel of Damag'd Cocheneal, out of the Mary Man of War ; together with the remaining Goods of the Little Galeon, called the Mary's Prize, consisting of 4 bags of Cocheneal, some Calcin'd Earth, Pictures, Lackered Tea-Tables, Chocolat-Mills, White and Brown Sugar, Molosses, Nicaragua and Mahogany-Wood, West Indian Box, etc. Allotments of all which Goods are disperced this day, being Thursday the 25th Instant February. And on Wednesday the 17th of March, at 9 in the morning, will be likewise exposed to publick Sale by the Candle, at the said Hall, the Cargo of the Galeon called the Tauro, or the Somerset's Prize, consisting of Snuff, Tobacco, Sugar, Cocoa, Ven-elles, Cocheneal, Cafia, Hydes, China Wares, Silk Grass, Brazelletto, Mahogany, Ebbone and Logwood, etc. Allotments whereof will be timely disperced, and all the Goods may be viewed at the Prize-Office Warehouses at Buttolph-Wharf, 3 days before the respective days of Sale.

The following details for the years 1720–30 are of particular interest, not only as proving the early imports of mahogany to London, but also as showing that the Colonial merchants from North America were even at this time conducting an active trade between the West Indies and England :

London. Imports. Christ. 1729–Christ. 1730.
Carolina.   No.
Wood Mahogany Plank 595 &
Ton
41–8 at 7–10 to 8–10 £360.19s.

Jamaica.   No.
Wood Mahogany Plank 2066.
Ton   £   s
& 214 at 8 Ton & 1 Plank £1815–6.

New Providence Ton   £
Wood Mahogany 20 & 8 Ton £160.

New York.
Wood Mohogony Plank 13 At 7–10
       £ s
to 8–10 Ton £104.

St. Xophera.   £
Wood Mohogany 1″ 12″ 0″ 0″ At 8
Ton £12–16.

Virginia & Maryland.   £
Wood Mohogany 20 Ton At 5 to 9
Ton £140.

It is not generally known that of all the West Indies, Jamaica was in the seventeenth and eighteenth centuries the chief source of mahogany for export to the Mother Country. John Ogilby, in 1671, wrote a book entitled *America, Being the Latest and Most Accurate Description of the New World.* Of Jamaica he says :

Here also great variety of Dyewoods, as Brasiletto, Fustick, Redwood, a kind of Log-wood, and several others, and rich sorts of woods, as Cedar, Mothogeney, Lignum vitae, Ebony, Granadilla, and others, which are frequently exported.

The *History of Jamaica*, written by Edward Long and published
in 1774, shows the prices of mahogany in the island of Jamaica
in the 1770's :

> The superior value of the Jamaica wood, for beauty of colouring,
> firmness, and durability, may therefore be easily accounted for ;
> but, as a large quantity of balks and planks is brought from the
> Spanish American coasts to this island, to be shipped from thence
> to Great Britain, the dealers are apt to confound all under the name
> of Jamaica wood, which in some measure hurts the credit of this
> staple production. The tree grows tall and strait, rising often sixty
> feet from the spur to the limbs ; the foliage is a beautiful deep
> green ; and the appearance, made by the whole tree, so elegant,
> that none would be more ornamental for an avenue, or to decorate
> a plantation.

It is recorded that in the year 1770 there were exported from
Jamaica 15,675 pieces of mahogany—8500 ft. cube to a value of
£50,000. By piecing together like a jigsaw puzzle all these
records and quotations from such varied sources, a picture can
be drawn of the birth and growth of an organized mahogany
trade, dating from those far-away days in the year 1695, when
Celia Fiennes first saw her " sweete outlandish wood " in the
house of Admiral Russell.

Thomas Sheraton, in *The Cabinet Dictionary*, published in
1803, has much to tell us of the West Indies mahogany trade.
It would appear that by this time mahogany was well established
in Great Britain, for he writes :

> Of all woods, mahogany is the best suited to furniture where
> strength is demanded. It works up easily, has a beautiful figure
> and polishes so well that it is an asset to any room in which it may
> be placed. Other woods used for cabinetwork are quite laid by
> since the introduction of mahogany.

He relates that Santo Domingo (Hispaniola) produced wood
of a hard texture, but not much used in this country except for
chairs. There seems to be some confusion in Sheraton's mind
regarding Cuba and Spanish Mahogany, and he writes of Cuba
as follows :

> A kind of mahogany somewhat harder than Honduras wood,
> but of no figure in the grain. It is inferior to Spanish wood, though
> probably the Cuba and Spanish mahogany are the same, as the

island of Cuba is a Spanish colony. . . . That, however, which is generally distinguished by Spanish mahogany is finer than what is called Cuba, which is pale, straight grained, and some of it only a bastard kind of mahogany. It is generally used for chair wood, for which some of it will do very well.

It would appear that in the early days Cuba mahogany trees were purchased in small groups from landowners and farmers at

CAMP SCENE, SHOWING MAHOGANY-TREES BEING FELLED IN HONDURAS (1851)
From a print of 1851.

prices ranging from one to four dollars a tree, according to quality and size. Somewhat surprisingly, the fellers were principally whites. These men, an old writer tells us, reversed the usual practices by drinking nothing else but strong coffee, and using rum as their principal remedy for wounds, bruises, and sprains of all sorts. Also, apparently, they held to the ancient belief recorded by Pliny, and insisted on felling the trees on a waning moon, it being held that the trees then came down sounder and of a richer colour. The logs were loaded upon carts, and then dragged by six, seven, or even ten yoke of oxen to the nearest river, subsequently to be floated to the coast.

It is said that the basis of measurement in the old days was the Spanish vara of 3 ft. 12 inches, which was considered by the traders to be equal to 33 English inches. Was this the primitive equivalent to the Liverpool measurement allowance ? This may be so, because an old writer says it is far more profitable to purchase large logs than small, because then the buyer obtains a bigger advantage under the system of measure ! Honduras, in the seventeenth and eighteenth centuries, was a Spanish possession. There is no record at that time of wood being exported direct from any of the Spanish Colonies to England. On the other hand, there is plenty of evidence that Jamaica acted as an entrepôt for this trade. Her merchants bought from the Spaniards in Honduras and the islands, then traded the mahogany to British merchants and to North America. The development of this entrepôt business was encouraged by an Act of Parliament passed in 1725 imposing a duty of £8 a ton on all foreign timber, including mahogany, imported into Great Britain. Spanish mahogany, however, occurs so infrequently in the Customs Returns that it can only be assumed that it was disguised under the general title of Jamaica wood ! In fact, the Jamaican Legislature attempted to take their ' rake-off ' on the business by placing duty on all wood of Spanish origin imported into that island. History relates that this Act had very little success. The coastline of Jamaica offered too many facilities for ' mahogany-running ' ! The *History of Jamaica*, published in 1774, gives this table :

An estimate of one year's produce, via. Prime Cost Jamaica currency.
510,000 feet Mahogany at 50s. per hund.   £12,750.
    Exports to North America
  10,000 feet Mahogany   250.
    Exports to Great Britain
500,000 feet of mahogany   12,500.

No doubt much of the timber listed in the Customs Returns as Jamaican was from the Spanish mainland. It is certain that by the end of the eighteenth century Honduras Mahogany as such was well known and esteemed in England. Sheraton knew the wood intimately, and in *The Cabinet Dictionary*, he states :

From this province is imported the principal kind of mahogany in use amongst cabinet-makers, which generally bears the name of

LOADING MAHOGANY LOGS ON OX-WAGONS IN HONDURAS (1850)

From a print of 1851.

Honduras mahogany, and sometimes Bay-wood, from the bay or arm of the sea which runs up to it. The difference between Honduras and Spanish wood is easily perceived by judges, but not by others unskilled in wood. The marks of the former are, as to size, its length and width, which generally run much more than in the latter wood. We seldom import any much more than 2 feet 2 inches broad and 10 feet long, and generally not more than 21 or 22 inches broad. Honduras wood will frequently run 12 to 14 feet in length, and from 2 to 4 feet wide. In rare instances, there have been some 6 or 7 feet over. The grain of Honduras wood is of a different quality from that of Cuba, which is close and hard, without black speckles, and of a rosy hue, and sometimes strongly figured ; but Honduras wood is of an open nature, with black or grey spots, and frequently of a more flashy figure than Spanish. The best quality of Honduras wood is known by its being free from chalky and black speckles, and when the colour is inclined to a dark gold hue.

A Mr McGregor, writing in a Parliamentary Report on the Spanish American Republics, tells us that the season for cutting Honduras Mahogany commenced in August. A party of fellers amounting to twenty or thirty men would work under the leadership of a captain. The most important person in the party was the huntsman, who went out at the beginning of the season to search the forests for suitable trees. The method of the huntsman was to climb the tallest tree he could find, from which he would take a bird's-eye view of the surrounding country and earmark suitable trees. This he was able to do more easily because at this season of the year the leaves of the mahogany-tree are of a yellow-reddish colour, and hence to be distinguished by the expert eye. We are told that such was the woodmanship of these hunters that, having come down from their lofty perches, they were able infallibly to make their way through the thick jungle to the trees that they had seen. As in the case of Cuba, the logs were dragged to the river-bank by large teams of oxen. They were then put into the river and floated down to the coast on the spring floods.

It is probably not generally realized that towards the end of the eighteenth century mahogany was used quite extensively for shipbuilding and repairs, particularly on the West Indian station. A notable example was the line-of-battle *Gibraltar*, built in the West Indies round about 1750. It is this ship which is mentioned in Admiral Sir Jahleel Brenton's memoirs, when he is quoted as saying :

> When I was First-Lieut. of the " Gibraltar," a huge three-decker, I narrowly escaped having been driven on an iron bound coast during a fearful gale of wind, which had forced her from her moorings, and that all efforts would have been fruitless unless

COUNTRY CART DRAWN BY OXEN AND LOADED WITH MAHOGANY LOG, CUBA
Early nineteenth century.
From a print of 1851.

the vessel had been of very singular construction, viz. Spanish built with her lower part one enormous mass of solid mahogany.

A writer of this period makes the point that shipowners prefer ships built of mahogany ; however ancient or worn such ships may become, the intrinsic value of this mahogany is much greater than that of any other wood. We are further told that the Spanish shipbuilders succeeded in constructing ships of mahogany timbers, which, having been captured, were found in commission in the British Navy a hundred years later. These old Spaniards selected wood which was firm, tough, and ' roey ' for the outside strakes, while soft or cedar-like boards were used for the inside linings and cabin fittings.

In 1846 a memorandum was prepared by the mahogany merchants of London and Liverpool and presented to the Admiralty and other Government Departments. This memorandum complained that owing to some apparent prejudice on the part of Lloyd's Committee and Inspectors they employed, mahogany did not receive the same consideration for shipbuilding purposes

FLOATING MAHOGANY LOGS DOWN THE RAPIDS, CUBA
Early nineteenth century.
From a print of 1850.

as British and African Oak (Iroko), East India Teak, and other woods. Apparently, the Inspectors employed by Lloyd's found some difficulty in drawing up an adequate specification to cover the various grades and quality of mahogany. A number of supporting documents were appended to the memorandum, among them a testimonial from a number of London mahogany merchants, as follows :

Appendix No. 6.   LONDON, 18th. Oct. 1845

We, the undersigned, having been long practically acquainted with the cutting up of Honduras Mahogany, do certify that the plank becomes more and more hard according to the time it is exposed to the air, that it is very durable, is not subject to dry rot, and after seasoning does not shrink. We accordingly recommend it for shipbuilding purposes :

Richard Goodman, having known the wood for		50 years
Joseph Belletti	,,	,,	40 ,,
John Lilley	,,	,,	45 ,,
Wm. Andrews	,,	,,	10 ,,
Thos. Bennett	,,	,,	28 ,,
T. Gabriel & Sons	,,	,,	35 ,,
N. Saxton	,,	,,	18 ,,
Truely & Company	,,	,,	30 ,,
Chas. Shadbolt & Company	,,	20 ,,
Jas. Latham	,,	,,	30 ,,
Wm. Locks	,,	,,	12 ,,
Benj. Ingram	,,	,,	56 ,,
T. Newton & Sons	,,	,,	50 ,,
Wm. Smith	,,	,,	30 ,,
W. S. Turnley (Honduras Mahogany has considerably more buoyancy than Oak or Teak, and not liable to splinter by a shot) having known the wood for		30 ,,
T. R. & W. Browning & Co. having known the wood for	45 ,,
W. Oliver	,,	,,	30 ,,
John Wood	,,	,,	30 ,,

We take the liberty of giving this list *in extenso* because it fixes beyond all dispute the age of a number of eminent timber families still engaged in the trade. It will be seen that the document is dated London, October 18, 1845, and on that date T. Gabriel and Sons declare that they had known mahogany for thirty-five years ; Jas. Latham for thirty years ; T. R. and W. Browning and Co. for forty-five years, and William Oliver for thirty years. Our survey of the mahogany trade has brought us down to the middle of the nineteenth century. Mahogany, once the pride of the hand craftsman with his delicate touch and tools, now takes its proper place as a prime wood in the machine age.

Turning now for a moment from the mahogany trade to the mahogany trader, in person, we wonder how many of our readers have come across the rare pamphlet entitled *The Mahogany Foreign Timber Trade of Liverpool*, price 2*d.*, published in London in 1883 under the initials J. E. H. The writer of this pamphlet, besides having a pretty literary style, was evidently also a timber merchant of some perspicacity. We cannot do better than quote his opinion on salesmanship :

> The import of foreign and Colonial timber into Liverpool in 1882 amounted to 32 m. c.ft. of Mahogany. There arrived many cargoes, chiefly from Honduras, Tobasco, St Domingo and Cuba. I may here remark on the wonderful ability some men possess as salesmen, and on the mysterious influence their presence alone has over a man when face to face in a business transaction. From the hands of such a one, the shrewdest man—the hardiest buyer—cannot escape. His previous firm resolve " to go round the market before buying " is paralysed, he cannot tell why. The conquest over him is complete.

Readers interested in the story of the Liverpool timber trade should try to see a copy of this pamphlet. By the way, there is a copy in the Library of the British Museum. Besides the above short quotation, the author makes many racy comments on the nineteenth-century timber merchant and his methods of business.

But everything passes, and the monopoly of the American Continent as a sole source of mahogany was about to be challenged from another great continental area. It was in 1672 that Charles II granted to the Royal African Company their first Charter. The earliest trade of the Royal African Company consisted of slaves and gold, the unfortunate slaves being sold mainly to the colonists in America and the West Indies. So many famous goldfields have been discovered since those days that it requires an effort of the imagination to realize that the land later known as the Gold Coast got its name originally from the gold-dust which attracted traders to its shores. Mahogany was soon recognized among the rain-forests of West Africa by the early English merchants, many of whom, as mentioned above, also traded with the West Indies. It was not, however, until 1789 that the wood was first botanically classified as *Swietenia senegalensis* by the famous botanist Desrousseaux. The first man to differentiate between the American and West African species was Jussieu in 1830. He proposed that the name *Swietenia senegalensis* should be altered to *Khaya senegalensis*. Since those days, of course, other species of the genus Khaya have been

Unloading a Ship at West India Docks, at the Close of the Eighteenth Century
From a print in the Collection o the Port of London Authority.

established. *Khaya ivorensis* and *Khaya grandifolia* are among the most common.

As mentioned earlier in this chapter, there is some doubt about the exact identity of the name ' mahogany,' or ' mahogani,' as the great botanist Linnæus translated the word into Latin.

A LARGE LOG OF HONDURAS MAHOGANY BEING SOLD AT BIRKENHEAD
" *The Illustrated London News*," April 6, 1850.

Mr Balfour Gourlay, however, gives us an account of the origin of the term ' Khaya,' as denoting the mahoganies of West Africa. A nineteenth-century botanist, he says, on an expedition to West Africa, which was just being opened to explorers, saw a tree he could not identify. On asking the natives the name, they unanimously replied " Khaya." A specimen was accordingly sent to Kew with a statement that the native name was Khaya. The scientists at Kew found the sample belonged to a genus of the family Meliaceæ, hitherto unknown. The new species was accordingly named *Khaya senegalensis*. It was not until the botanist made a return visit to West Africa that he discovered to his surprise and consternation that " Khaya " translated into English means " I don't know " !

We are indebted to Mr Temple Dobell and Mr Walter MacFarlane for many details regarding the early days of the West African mahogany trade as it affected Liverpool. The earliest shipments came from Axim, on the Ghana coast, in the year 1880 and onward. The logs, produced by native cutters, were squared by adzes and frequently badly shaped and rough-looking. Consequently it was impossible to sell the parcels by forward contract, and merchants would buy only after inspection. Hence the custom of selling by public auction sale grew up. At first, as mentioned earlier, the auction sales were held on the open quay. Later Messrs Farnworth and Jardine, Chaloner, and Dobell all built sale-rooms in the old Canada Dock. Among early pioneer shippers were Miller Bros., who had been originally West India merchants. They established themselves in the Benin area, which district was known as the Oil Rivers up to 1891, and commenced shipping mahogany. Lagos Mahogany also found its way to Liverpool about this time, being in the shape of comparatively small logs 12″ to 18″ square. Up to this date export houses, both in Ghana and the Niger Delta, had taken their share in the trade by buying up the logs of the native producers. But towards the end of the nineteenth century a different picture presented itself, particularly in Nigeria. Substantial forest concessions were secured by English and Scottish companies, among whom were the Royal Niger Company, Alexander Miller Bros. and Co., W. B. McIver and Co., and John Holt. These newcomers worked their concessions method-ically under competent white supervision, although, of coures, the work of felling, squaring, and hauling the logs to the nearest river-creek was performed by native labour. These vastly im-proved methods naturally produced a much better article, and consequently the demand for African Mahogany in both the ports of Liverpool and London increased enormously. By the courtesy of the United Africa Company the writer has been shown a sketch map attached to the original lease signed in 1902 between John Grady, agent of W. B. McIver and Co., and Chief Ogodo, of Ogodo Town, near Sapele, in Southern Nigeria, for the plot of ground upon which the United Africa Company's plywood factory now stands. It would appear that in those early days there was a shortage of trained surveyors in the Colony, for the map is the work of a Master Mariner, Captain G. R. Dampier, who signs in the corner.

During the early 1900's other companies took a hand in the trade, among them the British West African Timber Company and McNeil Scott and Co. Mahogany from West Africa was now a very popular wood in Great Britain. Auction sales were held at regular intervals in both Liverpool and London. In the United States also the demand for African Mahogany was steadily growing. There was at this time no steamer line between West Africa and the States, so American dealers had to obtain their supplies from the auction sales. A number of Liverpool merchants undertook the particular trade of catering for the American market in figured and stripey logs. This was a highly specialized business which required expert knowledge of the market.

However, it was not long before American shipping companies saw the great possibilities of the Coast trade, and established a direct service with the United States ports. American operators took advantage of these ships, and sent their inspectors to buy logs and ship them direct. The well-known Mengel Company were among the first to establish a depot in Ghana. This American trade, however, was, and still is, largely confined to Ghana and French Equatorial Africa. The American traders never operated to any extent in Nigeria.

The mention of America brings to mind the large business in mahogany conducted by firms with their headquarters and sawmills situate in the U.S.A. Such companies conducted, and do conduct, very large-scale logging operations over many forest areas in Central and South America, such countries as Honduras, Mexico, Guatemala, Peru, and Nicaragua being notable in this trade. Some of these logs are sawn locally, but it is customary to bring a great proportion to mills in the U.S.A. Leading firms are the Freiberg Mahogany Company, with offices, sawmill, and veneer plant at New Orleans ; Messrs Ichabod T. Williams and Sons, with a large sawmill, yards, and veneer-cutting plant at New Jersey, near New York ; and Messrs Weissfricker at Pensacola.

At the Liverpool and London auction sales African Mahogany parcels were classified under their ports of shipment.

Consequently the sale catalogues read almost like a West African gazetteer—Axim, Secondee, Lagos, Benin, Sapele, Half Assinee, Grand Bassam, Grand Lahou, Gaboon, and Cape Lopez ! These names would still arouse a feeling of nostalgia in many a hardwood office even to-day.

CHAPTER X

TEAK AND THE EAST INDIA COMPANY

THE East India Company, and their overlords the British Admiralty, were originally attracted to the teak forests of Western India by their realization of the fact that teak was a first-class timber for shipbuilding. The first ship for the Royal Navy to be constructed entirely of teak was the 36-gun frigate *Pitt*, which in the year 1805 was launched at Bombay. Thereafter the supply of the timber to the dockyards was a continual preoccupation with the Navy Department. It appears that the native contractors were unreliable, and the Navy was continually pressing the Bombay Government to allow an agent to be stationed on the Malabar Coast to make its purchases direct. Here is a report from Mr Seppings, Surveyor of Shipping:

> Teak is the most durable, but differs very much in quality. I will first speak of Malabar Teak, of which there are two kinds, the Northern and Southern; the first is far superior in point of durability, but more difficult to procure, which I believe arises from the land carriage, or from its not being felled near the rivers and streams of the country.

The principal forests lay in the districts of Malabar, Canara, Travancore, and Gujirat. Under Tippoo Sahib, in 1784, the right of felling the timber had been created a royal privilege. Following upon the defeat of that tyrant, the Court of Directors in 1800 instructed the Bombay Government to take over these rights on behalf of the East India Company. Captain Watson was appointed Conservator, and he proceeded to reserve the teak forests entirely to the Government, prohibiting all private felling. These measures caused great discontent, and so in 1822 the office of Conservator was abolished, and the forests were once more thrown open to the local timber merchants. The results were as could have been expected. To quote a contemporary official report, "in a few years the forests were in a state of dissolution." In these circumstances the Bombay Government in 1830 called upon the Indian Navy Board to submit a report on the teak forests of Malabar. They recommended the re-appointment of a Conservator, and a Mr Munro was appointed to the post.

The archives of the Governments of Bombay and Madras covering the period 1837–50 contain a long series of reports on the teak forests both from local Conservators and specially appointed officers. It is clear that the amount of action resulting

A Teak Log on a Country Ox-cart in the Time of Tippoo Sahib
From a print of 1861.

from all this paper-work was very small indeed. It is possible that the two Governments were torn between the desires of their officials to preserve and conserve the teak on the one hand, and the need to placate the Rajahs, landowners, and native timber merchants who rose in defence of their ancient rights. From these dusty reports much interesting information on the local native timber trade as practised from the days of the Great Mogul can be gathered. Mr G. A. Smith, Collector of the Rajahmundry District in 1838, tells us that merchants who desired to purchase the timber from the forests sent servants or agents to make advances to the hill people, who cut and delivered the timber to them on the banks of the Godaveri. The time for purchasing the timber was from December to June, the latter being the period when the freshes of the Godaveri allowed them to be brought easily down that river. The timber was formed

into rafts, fastened by chains, and turned adrift on the river to
float to the coast.

Again, in 1838 the Commissary-General at Bombay is found
inquiring from the Naval and Military Departments as to whether

PEASANTS CARRYING TEAK BILLETS FROM THE FOREST TO THE TOWN IN
THE TIME OF TIPPOO SAHIB

From a print of 1861.

he should procure a supply of large teak for frigates and line-of-
battle ships in anticipation of such vessels being built at Bombay
for Her Majesty's Service. The Government asked the opinion
of Admiral Sir Charles Malcolm, then Superintendent of the
Indian Navy. This gentleman in his turn called for a report
from Captain Harris of the Indian Navy, who in 1828–29 had
been Timber Agent in Malabar, and was said to have displayed
much local enterprise. This officer advised that the local Rajahs
should be invited to supply the required timber, as they had the
elephants and transport to convey it to the coast. Further, that

SHIPPING OFF THE MALABAR COAST
From a print by James Forbes, 1775.

an inspector should be stationed in Malabar to inspect the timber. The Government of India and the Honourable Company were doing their best to reduce the forest territories to order. But they continually had to balance their desire for commercial timbers against those problems of all native administrators— namely, shifting cultivations, grazings, and the needs of the local population for firewood.

Reports continued to be demanded by the Government, and in 1840 a Lieutenant Threshie is found giving what is probably the first account of girdling teak-trees. He writes :

> A merchant or forester purchases a right to fell the number of trees he may consider equal to his means of transport for the next two or three years, procures a permit or order for the same from the owner, and sends the people with whom he may have con- tracted or merely engaged at a certain rate per tree [about one rupee] to the forest, when the operation of cutting commences. This operation is described as cutting round the tree from about the height of a man's shoulders, the hatchet being more easily wielded at that height. The girth of the tree, as in the Tenasserim Provinces, determines the depth of the cutting. The trees are then allowed to remain in this half-cut state for a greater or less period, according as the merchant requires a fresh supply of timber to meet the demands ; however, one season is actually necessary, that the sap may be sufficiently absorbed to render it capable of being trans- ported and floated down the river ; some trees remain two or three years in the forest, and again on the coast a year or two. It was stated to be the interest of the merchant to have the timber well seasoned, as otherwise the expense and trouble of conveying it down the river was greater.

The first Burmese War in 1826 resulted in the Tenasserim Provinces of Moulmein, Tavoy, and Mergui being acquired by Great Britain. Immediate steps were taken to expand the teak trade of Moulmein. Also a number of shipbuilding yards were established, so that between 1830 and 1855 no fewer than 123 vessels were launched, practically all constructed of teak. The Navy was, as ever, conservative, and at first there was some prejudice shown against the Burmese teak. It was, however, as early as 1827 that Dr Wallich, a former superintendent of the Calcutta Botanical Gardens, was deputed to report upon and examine the Tenasserim teak forests of Lower Burma. He went up the Irrawaddy river as far as Ava, and saw the Salween forests. In those days the teak regions extended northward from the Province of Amherst, along the Salween river into the Karenee country ; from the delta of the Irrawaddy to a considerable distance north of Ava, the most productive and valuable forests being upon the Sarrawaddi river. Dr Wallich strongly recommended that a Commissariat timber-yard should be established at Moulmein, and that the teak forests should be worked as a Government monopoly.

The forests were infested by buffaloes, tigers, and elephants. The villagers informed Dr Wallich that they had no fear of tigers, as they seldom attacked anybody who did not enter the jungle quite alone ; and " as a reason for this abstemiousness on the part of the tiger, they said that the population was so small that the beast had not yet become acquainted with the taste of human flesh." Poultry abounded in the jungles, where they were caught by the simple contrivance of " nooses attached to a string scarcely thicker than a pack thread " ; the villagers supplied Dr Wallich with several fresh fowls' eggs, which were of a " remarkably small size." In May 1828 a cargo of 511 logs of teak, valued at 6000 rupees, was conveyed in the Honourable Company's ship *Ernaad* from Tavoy to Calcutta, where shortly after its arrival it was sold by public auction at a loss of 250 rupees. This and other similar experiences somewhat damped the ardour of Government. Accordingly, in the following year they accepted the suggestions of Mr Maingy, Civil Commissioner of the Tenasserim Provinces, that the forests should be thrown open to private individuals.

The Government of Bengal was continually calling for reports on its new possessions. As early as 1842 the Court of Directors in London were found toying with the idea of forming teak plantations under the Company's own control. They accordingly called for reports from their local officers. All did not go well with the young plantations, and long reports deal with the difficulties experienced in getting them fairly started. The writer is not a forester, and therefore has difficulty in assessing the contemporary evidence, but among other troubles there was apparently great difficulty in getting the seeds to germinate. All kinds of expedients were tried, including roasting the seeds, because it had been observed that young teak saplings multiplied after forest fires ! Mr Graham, a conservator, is found writing :

> Not being satisfied with the above process of preparing seeds for sowing, I applied fire to a few of the seeds, and found from the trial that the coating covering the shell acted like turf, which convinced me that in this process the seed inside of the shell must be destroyed, or in a manner roasted, and therefore be rendered unfit for vegetation ; I then threw a few of the seeds into water to see what effect the water had on them. I found on this trial that the coating acted something like a sponge, and contained as much water as convinced me that the shell and seed must rot before the time usual for the seed's vegetation, which is mentioned in the tehseeldar's letter to be forty days. Being unable to get any useful information on the subject from any of the proprietors of forests, in this part of the country, and being convinced that the shell ought to be cleared of the outside spongy coating before being put into the ground ; in beds of about sixteen yards long and one and a quarter broad, along with fourteen thousand prepared by fire, the whole covered with a light coating of hay, and in sixteen days after they had been put into the ground on removing the old hay to replace it with fresh, I discovered that five of the seeds cleared with the knife and one of those prepared by fire had vegetated.

Mr Graham, in an effort to imitate Nature, was even reduced to experimenting with white ants to clean his seeds.

M. Perottet, a French botanist on the way to Pondicherry, was asked to inspect the nurseries, and, needless to say, he put in his report. The Frenchman favoured the reproduction of young trees by means of shoots and suckers. But he was a modest man, for in conclusion he says that his suggestions should be submitted " to a man instructed in vegetable physiology and arboriculture." Obviously a primitive silviculturist ! At this stage Mr Conolly, another conservator, appears in charge of the young plantations. He finds it all too much for him on top of his other duties, and appeals to the Government for the services of a trained forester. Fortunately for Mr Conolly, the Marquis of Tweeddale, Governor of Madras, was a great Scottish nobleman with considerable landed interests. In a Minute dated the 8th of December, 1846, this is what his Lordship says :

> I have had much experience in plantations and woods on my own account at home as well as in those of other proprietors, but

I never saw a better commencement than in the Government teak plantations of Malabar.   The proximity to water-carriage, the gradual clearing of jungle towards the interior for security to health, and to prepare for extending the plantation into the interior, the education of so many workmen and " maistries," not only for working the plantations, but also for the management of the natural woods (and making good roads of communications as the plantations advance), are all objects of essential consequence to future success in a new undertaking, and have all been carefully attended to.

But Lord Tweeddale recognizes that there is still much to be done far beyond the capacity of the overworked Mr Conolly ! The Minute concludes with this recommendation :

In my own opinion also it appears impossible for Mr Conolly to give sufficient attention to so large a concern, and I do not see how either the plantations or the forests can have justice done to them without the constant supervision of an experienced European eye.   I would not remove the duty from his charge, but I would allow him a practical forester, whose time and attention should be given under Mr Conolly's direction to the management of the plantations and forests, and if found practicable and advisable, his attention might likewise be directed to the growth of Cardamums, Cinnamon, and other spice and valuable timber-trees.

The India Office files and reports of the beginning of the nineteenth century reveal many illuminating facts concerning the struggles of the early forestry officers to bring the Indian forests under control and establish plantations.   It is hoped that enough has been written here to whet the appetites of those who may wish to study further this interesting field.

In 1841 Captain O'Brien, of H.M. 63rd Regiment, was sent to survey the Tenasserim forests.   His report is especially interesting as giving an indication of the commercial firms, both European and otherwise, actually at work in the forests.   Mr Wales had a grant of 500 trees.   Beyond Mr Wales' boundary a native had felled 500 trees without any grant whatever !   On the Upper and Lower Tyghee, Messrs Cockerell and Co. had grants covering about 1500 trees, while on the Kyoon Geown, Messrs Darwood and Co. had a forest with about 300 trees.   On the Goonjee and Natchoung tributaries the grants were held by Messrs Agar and Richardson, but the teak was somewhat inferior. On the Mittigate was a fine forest which had been granted to Captain Biden and a native of Calcutta named Annund Chunder Mittire, and the upper part contained about 4000 trees. Other grants were Goonjee Forest, held by Mr Richardson ; Megwa Forest, held by Captain Clarke ; Natchoung Forest, held by Mr Agar. It will be seen that the concessionnaires were a mixed bag, and the names included a number of retired Army and Navy officers.

In 1842 the Government called upon Mr Seppings, their Surveyor of Shipping, for his views on the respective merits of Malabar and Moulmein Teak. He has a decided preference for the Malabar wood, although he grants that Moulmein may be used if selected carefully. All descriptions of teak, says Mr Seppings, are proof against white ants ; whereas all other descriptions of timber are liable to the attacks of this destructive vermin. He relates that the Honourable Company's ship the *Ganges* came into the Dockyard for survey. Her timbers, apart from teak, were found to be riddled by the destructive ants, and this although a thorough examination made four years previously had proved the ship to be quite free at that time. Then Mr Seppings gives an account of what must surely be a very early example of the use of steam as a pest-destroyer in wood :

> The ' Ganges,' previous to this opening out had been steamed to a very great extent for nearly two days ; the hull, previously to being steamed, was made perfectly air tight ; to such a degree was it carried that the very dammer was melted out of the seams of the deck, and where the caulking was bad, the steam issued out from the top sides. I mention this fact, because it has been positively asserted that steam will exterminate the white ants ; so far from this being the case, I could, if necessary, give other instances where it had failed equally as much as in the ' Ganges.'

A further milestone in the history of teak was the Second Burmese War in 1852. It was then that Great Britain acquired the province of Pegu and its important forests. In 1856 Dr Brandis was placed in charge as Conservator, and plans were laid for systematically working the timber. Dr Brandis was a determined and outstanding personality. He made several tours, and a number of comprehensive reports were filed by him. He found a Burmese trade in existence, but untrustworthy and inefficient. Here is his comment :

> Thus the contracts concluded for this year were made with parties of very different classes and occupations ; for out of the twenty-four contractors engaged were :

Myookes	1
Tikthagees	2
Subordinates of the Forest Dept.	11
Burmese timber merchants	4
Persons of particular trade	1
Foresters from Moulmein	5
Total ..	24

In order to improve this state of things, a number of Moulmein foresters must be induced to come over to this province with their elephants, and enterprising inhabitants of this country must purchase a number of these animals, without which timber of good sizes cannot be brought down from our forests.

But at least one large European firm was already working, for in the year 1854 Messrs Fowle and Co. purchased from the Government 12,512 logs, and actually removed 9615 logs. This firm is frequently mentioned as large operators. The first preoccupation of Dr Brandis was to clean up his forests so that an effective working plan and system of annual girdling could be put into operation. He tells us that in 1856, 13,080 logs were brought out by nine contractors employing in all about a hundred elephants, and a further fifteen smaller contractors using buffaloes. Dr Brandis drew up most comprehensive and exact rules for working the forests under his charge. But he was a broadminded man, and realized that the new order might press hard on the local inhabitants. The following paragraph shows his attitude :

> Under Burmese rule, timber for building zayats, Poungyee Kyoungs, bridges, and other works for religious or benevolent purposes, was free from all taxes and dues, and the fact that under the present rule, in the interior it has been made impossible, and on the large rivers very difficult, to procure a supply of that timber which in their estimation is alone worthy of being employed for such purposes, is perhaps one of those privations to which the Burmese population of this country is most alive. A better opportunity could scarcely be found, to reconcile the minds of the people

to the present forest laws, than the adoption of liberal measures in this respect. In common justice this liberality must be extended to Christian places of worship, and schools in the Kareen and Burmese Christian villages in the district. This measure together with its mode of execution is embodied in No. XIX of the new forest rules.

In January 1858 Mr James Barker was appointed Head Assistant of the Forest Department, Tenasserim and Martaban Provinces. He was an active man and much commended by his Superintendent for his judgment and firmness. Under his orders 9564 teak logs were dragged by the Karens to the river-bank and delivered to Messrs Gravemen and Co. of Moulmein. The amount paid to the Karen foresters for their labours was 47,800 rupees, while the timber realized 89,920 rupees, showing a nice little profit to Government of 4 rupees 6 annas 5 pies per log ! In 1859, 2771 logs were collected and sold for 23,960 rupees. The Karen foresters were paid 11,980 rupees—profit per log as worked out by the office, 4 rupees 5 annas 2 pies. Between 1847 and 1860 the Karens moved to the river-bank 50,457 logs, for which they were paid in all 247,031 rupees, while the timber fetched 366,249 rupees. These are transactions of some magnitude, and show the size that the teak trade had already reached in this area alone.

Apart from Messrs Todd, Findlay, and Co., the following names of contractors appear in Mr Barker's reports—Mr Warwick, Moung Chai, Mr Arietick, Nga Taubien. We are given some interesting details of the practical methods of securing the wood in those early days. It appears that a well-trained elephant, in good condition, could be expected to drag to the riverside about 150 logs, averaging one ton each, in one season. The preparation and handling of the timber by the contractors were extremely rough and primitive. Trees were felled 5 to 10 ft. from the ground. The foresters were in the habit of cross-cutting all the logs at 18 or 30 ft., regardless of their shape, whereas by converting timber in intricate localities into shorter pieces much fine wood could have been brought out.

Already primitive sawmills were being installed in the forest areas. Here is Dr Brandis' Minute on such a proposition :

The base of this hill would be an excellent place for the erection of a water sawmill, which might be put up at very little expense

As most of the machinery is made of wood, the water-wheel, etc. etc. could be made on the spot. All that would require to be brought up would be the multiplying power, say one large cast-iron wheel, one small ditto, commonly known by the name of pinion, and a few iron gudgeons (say 4) with the same number of brass or bellmetal bushes (the latter could almost be dispensed with, as good hard wood for that purpose is to be found in the forests— beech is usually used at home), some bolts and nails, circular saws with their iron axles, all this could be put together by any common workman, without the assistance or expense of an engineer, which is necessary for the erection of steam mills, and also for their working, after they are erected. The use of such a mill would be to square large logs, convert the slabs into boards or shingles for the roofing of houses, saw up logs into scantlings, etc. etc. This would be an immense saving to Government.

Gradually Dr Brandis, an energetic and capable administrator, introduced new methods and order into the districts under his control. A Forest Act was signed in 1865 which marked the virtual establishment of the Burma Forest Department, once a landmark in Empire forestry. Permits, concessions, and leases were abolished, and the forests of Lower Burma were worked departmentally.

The Third Burmese War of 1885, culminating in the banishment of the notorious King Thebaw, had important repercussions on the teak trade of Upper Burma. At the time of his accession the King had renewed the leases granted by his father, King Mindoon, to the British teak operators, prominent among whom were the Bombay Burmah Trading Corporation, Ltd (B.B.T.C.L.). Soon, however, Thebaw, aided and abetted by the French Consul, M. Haas, a most ambitious man, proceeded to put all kinds of difficulties in the way of the British firms. M. Haas set to work to negotiate a treaty between France and the King, under which the French, among a number of things, were to establish a State Bank, take over the ruby-mines, and operate the great teak forests of Upper Burma. This treaty, signed by King Thebaw, fell into the hands of the British, and a précis was telegraphed to London, where its contents were conveyed to Lord Salisbury, the then Foreign Secretary.

Thus, perhaps for the only time in history timber traders found themselves at the focal point of a war. For within a few months an Expeditionary Force was dispatched from India and proceeded up the river Irrawaddy in boats to occupy Mandalay. This was the occasion of Rudyard Kipling's famous poem *Mandalay*, first published in 1890 in *The Scots Observer* :

> Come you back to Mandalay,
> Where the Old Flotilla lay.
> Can't you hear their paddles chunkin' from Rangoon to Mandalay.

Opinions as to the exact cause of the Third Burmese War may differ as to whether it was King Thebaw's barbarity in massacring his relations, their wives and children, or the ambitions of the Frenchman Haas, or the wrongs of the teak traders. It is clear, however, that the Bombay Burmah Trading Corporation, Ltd, have always disclaimed that the war was made on their behalf. Those who like their history spiced with romance cannot do better than read that enthralling novel *The Lacquer Lady*, by F. Tennyson Jesse. Here is all the colourful life of the last days of King Thebaw's Burmese Court at Mandalay, with the names of the principal European characters in the drama but thinly disguised. The reader can also enjoy the novelist's version of the story of the disappointing love affair of poor Fanny Bagshaw, who is said to have conveyed the secret copy of the fatal French treaty into the hands of the British. Although the war was quickly over, many of the teak traders found themselves temporarily in positions of great danger. Several members of the B.B.T.C.L. staff lost their lives at the hands of infuriated Burmese. The great Corporation lent every possible aid to the Expeditionary Force. Many of their Karen forest guards were employed as scouts and runners. At least one member of the B.B.T.C.L. staff served as a volunteer on the famous flotilla. Here is a quotation from the contemporary diary of Mr Alfred MacDonald :

> For the next day or two we steamed on and when approaching Ava a large Burmese loung or Royal canoe was seen coming down stream waving a white flag ; this turned out to be one of the King's Ministers, sent to ask for terms of peace. He went on board the General's steamer and terms were discussed, and he was sent back to say that there must be total surrender, and that the King must give himself up, otherwise Mandalay would be destroyed. Next day word was sent down that the King agreed and the Flotilla

KING THEBAW'S PALACE AT MANDALAY, SHOWING DETAILS OF THE CARVED TEAK CONSTRUCTION

By courtesy o the Bombay Burmah Trading Corporation, Ltd.

proceeded with full steam to Mandalay, where all troops were landed, in full marching order. Mandalay City lies about two and a half miles back from the river and is a walled city, four miles square, surrounded on all sides by a deep moat. The wall is very picturesque, being about thirty feet in height and ten to fifteen feet thick ; the gate-ways, watch-towers and minarets are all beautifully carved in Burmese Teak. The Palace Enclosure, which is inside another wall, is in the centre of the city and is surrounded by gardens which, although small, are very pretty, fruit trees having been planted and cultivated freely. There are four gates into the City, one on each side, and the triumphal entry of the troops was arranged so that a force should enter at each of the four gates about the same time.

In reconstructing the early history of the Burma teak trade we are much indebted to the Bombay Burmah Trading Corporation, Ltd, for permission to use their records and the diaries of their forest managers. This renowned firm owe their origin to the family business of Wallace and Co., trading in Bombay in the 1850's. This partnership consisted of six brothers, and the eldest, William Wallace, interested himself in the teak trade. In 1862 he accompanied the Commissioner of Burma, Sir Arthur Phayre, to Mandalay on the occasion of the signing of a trade treaty with King Mindoon. It appears that the King took a great liking to the Scotsman, so that when William Wallace asked for permission to work teak in Upper Burma, Mindoon personally recommended to him the Ningyan area, later known as the Forest of Pyinmana. However, the firm of Wallace and Company could not see their way permanently to finance the teak business. Consequently, when in 1864 the American Civil War brought prosperity to Bombay owing to the rise in the value of cotton the firm took advantage of the resultant boom to transfer the timber business to a new company, first called the Burmah Trading Company, later to become the Bombay Burmah Trading Corporation, Ltd. It is interesting that the assets handed over by William Wallace in 1864 comprised :

> Permits to work teak in Upper Burma, two small teak forests on the Attaran River, sawmills at Dallah in Rangoon and at Natmoo in Moulmein, office and godowns in the Strand Road, and a piece of land at Poozoondoung in Rangoon, and ninety elephants, of which seventeen are employed in the mills and seventy-three in forest work.

Quite a nice little inventory, even if rather mixed ! Among other firms working in Burma in those early days were Gladstone, Wylie, and Co., and Bulloch Bros. and Co., both of Rangoon ; the Burma Company, Ltd ; Todd, Findlay, and Co.; Macgregor ; and Steel Brothers. Shipments from Rangoon and Moulmein to Europe were made by sailing-ships up to the beginning of the 1880's. The first steamer, the *Elginshire*, was chartered by the B.B.T.C.L. in 1884 to carry a full cargo of teak from Rangoon to the Clyde at 70s. per ton. A great name in the Burma teak trade was the British India Steam Navigation Company, which once headed all the merchant-shipping firms in the world in point of tonnage. In their early days the B.I.S.N. Company had two steamers, the *Byculla* and the *Colaba*, specially built for the carrying of teak. Before the coming of steam saw-mill plant to Burma most of the teak production consisted of hand-sawn, hewn, adzed, or dubbed squares and planks. The

EUROPEAN FOREST OFFICER SUPERINTENDING THE FELLING OF TEAK-TREES
IN THE JUNGLE

By courtesy of Professor E. P. Stebbing.

sawmill at Dallah transferred by William Wallace in 1864 was said to comprise a powerful steam sawmill in full working order. The plant included a new engine, two boilers, and four large frame-saws.

In those days, as now, the trees would be selected for girdling by the Forest Officer. When they were ready after some three

BURMESE RIVERMEN ON THE RIVER OUTSIDE THEIR FLOATING HOME

years the foresters would come along with their elephants, fell the trees, and log them into suitable lengths. An elephant would then drag the logs to the nearest stream. If an elephant thought the ground was too difficult and rough for him he would show his displeasure with loud groans and roars. Very often several elephants had to be put on one log to get it over a difficult place. The young forest assistants had a busy time, visiting the different camps, giving advances of pay to the foresters, and keeping count of the logs hauled out. The tours went on until the start of the hot weather in March or April. Then everybody had a holiday, even the elephants ! After reaching the main river the teak logs were made up into rafts of about a hundred, firmly lashed together with rattans. Each raft had a small hut built on it, where the raftsmen sheltered and slept. The crew had quite a comfortable time, except when they got into the dangerous rapids and whirlpools, of which there were a number on the great rivers. It was said that as much as twenty years might elapse between the girdling of a tree and its safe arrival at Rangoon, while over a thousand miles of water might have been covered in the wandering journey.

It is to be hoped that for their own pleasure many readers have seen that delightful musical play *The King and I*. If so, they will be interested to know that the charming if precocious boy Master Leonowens, there portrayed, played his part in the development of the teak trade of Siam. In fact, his name still survives in the firm of Leonowens and Co. of Bangkok, a subsidiary of Denny, Mott, and Dickson, Ltd. Here is a contemporary opinion on the matter :

> L. T. Leonowens was a man who had great influence with the Princes and Chiefs—his mother had been governess to King Chulalongkorn—he had great knowledge of the natives and their language.

Another interesting character in the Siamese teak trade was Dr Cheek, who originally was an American Mission doctor. He spoke the language fluently, and became so friendly with the royal princes that he even induced them to lend him money to exploit the teak forest. Other early comers were the Siam Forest Company, Windsor, Clarke, and Co., the East Asiatic Company, an old Siamese lady named Kun Mai Povak, and, of course, the B.B.T.C.L. There were also a number of Chinese Kongsees, or co-operatives, established in Bangkok. Chief of these was Kim Sing Lee, whose interests were later acquired by the B.B.T.C.L. There is no doubt that these Chinese traders had supplied the Chinese markets for immemorial centuries before the coming of the Europeans.

All the best teak forests of Siam were in the territories of the chiefs of the Laos States of Upper Siam, who were independent, except that they acknowledged the suzerainty of the King of Siam by sending him a golden flower as yearly tribute. In 1883 the teak exports from Siam to Europe were some 8000 tons, but by 1890 they had reached the figure of 22,000 tons. Fortunately for us, the B.B.T.C.L. sent the lively Mr MacDonald to represent them at Bangkok, and we cannot do better than quote again from his diary :

On King Chulalongkorn's return from his trip to Europe in 1898 the Chinese merchants gave him a great dinner and reception to which I was invited. We sat down to a dinner of some thirty courses, starting with birds nest soup, sharks' fins, snails' horns, special seaweed, etc. etc., and all without knives, forks or spoons— only two ivory chopsticks ! We Europeans found the soup with only chopsticks a bit of a puzzler, but the Chinese boy who was in attendance, showed us how to manipulate matters by holding the bowl in which the soup was served close to one's mouth and whipping the soup into the mouth as quickly as possible—and the soup was really very good, tasting like very delicious vermicelli, the sharks' fins were also quite nice. After dinner we were entertained in the grounds by an exhibition of fireworks, most of which had been taken out from Europe, including Brocks of London, wonderful rockets and lights, etc., and it was quite one of the best shows I have ever seen.

The Siamese teak trade has progressed steadily since those early pioneer days. Impressive sawmills have been established in Bangkok with modern machinery, and a large, efficient export trade has been developed both to Europe and the Far East.

CHAPTER XI

OAK, THE IMMEMORIAL WOOD

GREAT oak forests covered England and Wales for thousands of years before the country's recorded history began. One of the earliest historical records of oak-woods in Britain was made by the famous historian Pliny (c. 61–113) in his history of the Roman Empire. Among other things, he says :

> The Druids hold nothing so sacred as the mistletoe, and the tree on which it grows, provided it be an oak. They make choice of oak groves in preference to all others, and perform no rites without oak leaves ; so that they seem to have the name of Druids from thence, if we derive their name from the Greek.

Apart from Pliny, we have very few references as to how the forests of England were administered during the Roman occupation. It is reasonable to believe, however, that the Romans in Great Britain made clearances in forests only for military and agricultural purposes. But on the consolidation of their newly won territories by the Saxon invaders a number of forest codes and laws were promulgated by the Royal Councils, for the new invaders were great hunters. A law of King Ina (d. 726) stated that whoever set fire to a woodland should be fined £3 ; anyone who felled a tree without permission—and the sound of the axe was to be sufficient evidence—would be fined 30s. If, however, the tree was so large that thirty hogs could shelter in its shade, then the fine was doubled. Whoever felled a tree so as to block the King's highway would have to pay to the King the sum of £5.

Every schoolboy knows how addicted William the Conqueror and his heirs were to hunting, and it has been calculated that by the time of Henry III the Kings of England held as much as one-tenth of the country in their own right as royal forests or chases. The Norman Kings established special Courts of Justice to deal with forest affairs and offences, but here, again, it was the well-being of the hunted deer that was principally

concerned, rather than the stately oak. Things had reached
such a pass that several clauses of the Magna Carta were
devoted to righting the wrongs of those who lived in the
forest areas. It was enacted that all the bad customs relating to
forests, the exactions of sheriffs and their officers, should be immediately inquired into in every forest by twelve sworn knights,
who were to be chosen by the men of each county. It was, however, by John's successor, the well-meaning Henry III, that the
" Charte Forestie " was promulgated. This Charter, which is
by no means so well known as the famous Magna Carta, was
issued on February 10, 1225, and was devoted entirely to a
revision of forest laws. It contains no fewer than sixteen clauses,
some of which are devoted to establishing with certainty the
areas of land which the Crown could in future claim as forest-
land, together with clauses dealing with the rights of people
living in and around the forests. The tolls which the King's
forest officials might collect for traffic through the forest were
limited to twopence a year for each cart and a penny for a pack-
horse, these being levied only in the case of merchants who
entered the forest by licence to buy timber, underwood, and
charcoal. Peasants and others going about their normal business
were to pass freely. The severity of the preservation laws is
apparent from the interesting permission set out under Clause 11
regarding people passing through the forests on their way to
wait upon the King :

> Whatsoever archbishop, bishop, earl, or baron, coming to us
> at our commandment, passing by our forests, it shall be lawful for
> him to take and kill one or two of our deer, by view of our forester,
> if he be present, or else he shall cause one to blow a horn for him,
> that he seem not to steal our deer, and likewise they shall do in
> returning from us, as it is aforesaid.

To turn now from the study of oak as a forest tree to its use
as a highly prized timber for building and joinery, it is interesting
that in the year 1380 William Wyntryngham, described in documents as a carpenter, contracted to build a new chapel and houses
at the Duke's castle at Hertford for the sum of £440. This
amount was paid for the execution of the work alone, because
later we read that instructions were given to the Duke's Receiver
in Hertfordshire to fell twelve oak-trees and deliver them to the

Castle. In the spring of 1381 the Receiver was instructed to cut six oaks in the Wood of St Albans Abbey called Northaghwode, as a gift from the Abbot ; six oaks in the Bishop of Ely's Wood at Hatfield, being a gift from the Bishop ; and twelve oaks from the Duke's portion of Hertford Wood. It is also noteworthy to read that on this latter occasion the trees were to be felled under the surveyance of William Wyntryngham, so perhaps the first consignment of timber was not entirely to his satisfaction.

Meanwhile the work at King's College, Cambridge, a classic example of medieval craftsmanship, had been interrupted by the outbreak of the Wars of the Roses. However, in 1459 the work was restarted. In this connexion Master Carpenter Thomas Sturgeon was employed, but it is interesting that another principal carpenter, one Martin Prentice, was working at the same time, and from the entries in the accounts it seems that most of his time was spent in the woods dealing with the supply of oak. For instance, the accounts of May, June, and July in 1480 show him as superintending the felling of timber both at Stanstead Park, Essex, and in the woods belonging to the Monastery of Walden, Essex. The accounts show that he was in the woods at Walden again in October, but this time accompanied by the College Master Carpenter, John Sturgeon. The following year he was in the woods at Huntingdon, where payments were made to him and his workmen. It seems probable that he was here supervising the felling of the King's gift of timber from the forest at Weybridge close by the town ; while in July Martin Prentice and his gang were once more engaged in felling oaks and carting underwood from the royal forest at Sapley in the same district.

By the end of the fifteenth century the office of Purveyor of the King's Timber was created, and in 1513 we find one George Lord, who was given the above-mentioned title, supplying wood for work to be done at the Tower of London. There is also on record a disputed account of Lord's which was laid before the Council asserting that he had delivered five loads of timber to the Tower of London, and that one Thomas Stokton, a Master Carpenter, would not meet the bill. King Henry VIII in his seizure of the Church and monastic lands acquired a number of forests. Many woods and chases were given to courtiers, who proceeded to fell them for their own enrichment. Consequently,

in the seventeenth year of his reign an Act for the preservation of woodlands was passed, of which the following is the
preamble :

> The King our sovereign, perceiving and right well knowing
> the great decay of timber and wood universally within the realm
> of England, and that, unless a speedy remedy in that behalf be
> provided, there is a great and manifest likelihood of scarcity and
> lack, as well for building houses and ships, as for firewood ; it is
> enacted, that in copse of underwood felled at 24 years' growth
> there shall be left twelve standrells, or store oaks, on each acre, or
> in default of oaks, as many elm, ash, or beech, etc. ; and that they
> be of such as are likely trees for timber, and such as have been left
> at former fellings, if there have been any left before ; under pain
> of forfeiting of 3s. 4d. for every such standard not left, one half
> to the crown, and the other to the party who may inform.

If the coppice cut was under fourteen years old, then the land
had to be enclosed for no less than four years under a penalty of
3s. 4d. per rood for every month the enclosure was left undone.
No calves might be grazed in such an enclosure for two years,
and no mature cattle for four years. On the other hand, if the
woodland was from fourteen to twenty-four years of age, then
it had to be enclosed under the same terms for six years. The
felling of trees on commons was prohibited under a penalty of
6s. 8d. per tree. However, under a curious clause in the County
of Cornwall the trees might be felled if dead on the top and
standing within two miles of the sea, no doubt having regard
to the prevailing west winds in that part of the country, with
their deleterious effect on plantations.

Windsor Park is the shrunken core of Windsor Forest, which
once had a circumference of 120 miles. By Tudor times its area
had dwindled, and by the reign of James I it had sunk to a
circumference of 77 miles. The date of its enclosure as a Royal
Park is not exactly known, but in 1568 we find Sir William
Cecil petitioning for two French glass-makers to have the privilege of making charcoal in " Windsor Great Park." Windsor
Forest was noted for its fine oak-trees, a number of which were
felled from time to time and employed for work in the royal
castles and palaces. John Evelyn in his great book on forests
and forest trees, entitled *Sylva*, first published in 1664, has the

following to say about the respective qualities of various types
of oak :

> That which is twined and a little wreathed (easily to be discerned
> by the texture of the bark) is best to support burthens, for posts,
> columns, fumers, etc., for all which our English Oak is infinitely
> preferable to the French, which is nothing so useful, nor comparably
> so strong ; insomuch as I have frequently admired at the sudden
> failing of most goodly timber to the eye, which, being employed
> to these uses, does many times most dangerously fly in sunder, as
> wanting that native spring and toughness which our English Oak
> is endued with.

Sherwood Forest is almost as famous in English history as
Windsor Forest, and a list of officials appointed by letters patent
from the Crown is interesting. It comprised a Lord Warden,
a Bow-bearer and Ranger, four Verderers, a Clerk of the Swain-
mote (or Forest Courtier), a Beadle, and nine Keepers. Sherwood Forest had many fine oaks, and a number were felled for
use in notable public buildings. The Duke of Newcastle, to
whom Welbeck Abbey belonged, made a gift of his oak-trees
towards the rebuilding of St Paul's Cathedral following the Fire
of London in 1666. The following interesting letter is in existence from the famous architect Sir Christopher Wren to Mr
Richard Neale, the Duke's Steward :

For Mr Richard Neale,
Steward to His Grace the Duke of Newcastle,
at Welbeck.

Lond., April 4th, 1696

Sir,
  Having in my letter of June 23, 1695, signified to you a particular
of all the scantlings of the Timber wee might use in the roofe of
St Paules, that His Grace's noble benefaction might be as usefull
as may be to the worke, and understanding that what is already
designed is none of the Great beams, wch is what wee are most
sollicitous for, and being given alsoe to understand that wee must
expect this season but Ten of the great trees ; I presume once
more to acquaint you with the scantlings of the great Beames to
prevent mistake.
  47 feet long, 13 inches and 14 inches at the small end, growing
  timber, this scantling to hold die square, as neer as can be without
  sap.

Mr Longland, our chiefe Carpenter, will be sent down this season to take care of this concerne, & the timber brought down to Bawtrey, whom I desire you to converse with in particulars wch at this distance I can hardly determine, and beseech you to present with all advantage our utmost sence of his Grace's Favour, of wch also I am very sensible, as becomes.

Your humble servant,
C^{er} WREN

Another ancient forest, Whittlebury Forest, in Northamptonshire, was surveyed in 1620 by the Royal Commissioners, and was found to contain 50,046 sound oak-trees valued at £25,755, with 360 decayed trees valued at £123 6s. 8d. Assuming the trees to have contained about 50 ft. cube each, this gives a value standing of about 2s. per ft. cube. The Royal Commissioners produced another account in 1790 showing the quantity of naval timber taken from the same forest. This is very interesting :

The quantity of naval timber felled from 1772 to 1786 inclusive, was 3,158 loads, the produce of which, with the bark and offal wood, amounted to	£8,986.17. 4.
Fees, poundages, and expenses	1,338. 8. 3.
Clear produce of navy timber to that time......	7,648. 9. 1.
From 1786 to 1790, navy timber was cut as follows : 2,304 trees, 2,572 loads, and 19 feet, square measure, which, at the then customary measure of £1.18s. per load, together with the tops, bark, etc. amounted to............................	7,111. 16. 4.
2,022 dotard and decayed oaks, and 331 ash trees, sold for payment of officers' salaries...........	1,437. 14. 10.
	8,549. 11. 2.
Less expenses, salaries, etc......................	2,496. 1. 0.
Clear produce since 1786.....................	6,053.10. 2.
Ditto of Navy Timber, 1772 to 1786..........	7,648. 9. 1.
	13,701.19. 3.
Less for expenses, salaries, etc.	1,353. 1. 4½.
	£12,348.17. 10½.

Major Oak, Sherwood Forest, said to be the Trysting Tree of Robin Hood, and reputed to be 1500 Years old

Photo Charles R. Denton.

Referring to the requirements of the British Navy, we cannot refrain from giving a definition by a writer in the *Forestry Journal* on lop and top :

> Lop and Top is that part of the stem or body of the tree, stripped of the branches, which in navy timber is cut off by direction of the purveyor, as unfit for naval use ; and in stolen timber that part which the thief either voluntarily leaves behind him, or has not an opportunity of conveying away. It frequently happens that these tops contain timber fit for carpenters' or coopers' uses, and sometimes knees and crooked timbers fit for small vessels, but very rarely for king's ships. When they are unfit for any of these uses they are cut into cordwood.

It is not generally known that the New Forest at one time had a shipbuilding yard in the shape of Buckler's Hard, founded by the Duke of Montagu about 1720 as a port for the West Indian trade, the Duke owning the island of St Lucia. The largest ship built here was the *Illustrious*, with 74 guns, and it is known that three of Nelson's line-of-battle at Trafalgar were also built at Buckler's Hard—namely, the *Agamemnon*, the *Euryalus*, and the *Swiftsure*.

It seems that the problem of raising the quality of English oak specifications to that of imported graded oak, which is at the present moment very much concerning both the timber trade and the wood-consuming industries, is no new one. Mr Isaac Solly, a timber merchant giving evidence before the House of Commons about conditions in the trade during and following the Napoleonic Wars, stated that the price of English oak varied according to the thickness, 2″ plank being priced at £6 0s. 8d. per load and 4″ at £15 per load ; but he qualified his evidence by then stating that if English Oak plank was required of the same quality and dimensions as the selected Danzig Oak plank imported for joinery and shipbuilding purposes, then the prices he had given for English Oak would have to be doubled. In reply to a further question, Mr Solly stated that in any case it would not be possible to obtain the quantities of selected English Oak required to meet the demand. However, it emerged clearly in his evidence that the English Oak plank was considered to be more durable than the Danzig Oak variety, more especially where the construction had to be exposed to the combining

effects of wind and water. It is also an interesting fact that
when English Oak plank was used in such large quantities to
build up the sides of the great wooden ships it was customary,
rather than incur the waste of edging the plank to even width
throughout from butt to top, to edge the planks wedge-shaped.
This having been done, they were placed top to butt on the
sides of the ships, having the additional advantage of giving
greater strength, as all the joints, whether butt or side, would
be distributed. There is no doubt that the continual denudation
of the country's forests to supply oak timber required for the
maintenance of the Navy during the long wars of the eighteenth
century, culminating in the Napoleonic struggle, created great
anxiety in the minds of Government, and a number of Commis-
sions were appointed from time to time to inquire into the state
of the country's forests and woods, particularly those belonging
to the Crown. It is perhaps only natural that the Commissioners
were obliged to record a number of abuses in the way of neigh-
bouring landowners helping themselves to the Crown's trees,
and also the tendency for woodlands and chases to relapse into
mere common land. The Report of the Parliamentary Commissioners issued in 1792 says that the quantity of timber used
during the year 1788 for both the repairs to the Royal Navy
and the building of new ships amounted to 50,000 loads, or $2\frac{1}{2}$
million feet cube, of oak timber. The Commissioners went on
to give as their opinion that the present Crown forests and the
woods of private estates could no longer be relied upon to produce anything like such an annual quantity. They consequently
recommended that another 100,000 acres of oak plantations should
be planted within the next few years. This is very similar to the
course of events after the First World War, only then it was
softwoods.

It is not generally appreciated how early the trade in the
particular export of oak from the Baltic, known as " Wainscot "
logs, commenced. There is recorded in the Chancery cases of
the year 1400 the petition of Robert-atte-Woode and other
English merchants that they were wrongfully imprisoned by the
" Burghers of the Hanse " of Danzig while buying " Waynescotes " in the forests beyond that city. Danzig and Riga Wainscot Oak was freely imported into Great Britain during the
sixteenth and seventeenth centuries. Many examples of the wood

can be seen in the halls, libraries, and chapels of our older universities. Once upon a time the same could be said about the City of London Livery Halls, but now, alas, since the War their numbers are sadly diminished. On being asked, the Curator may well reply that it is " Norwegian Oak," thus giving life to the tradition of the stout little ships of Norway that transported the Baltic wood from the ports of Riga, Danzig, and, to a less degree, Memel.

This trade specification of Wainscot logs was peculiar to the British and Dutch markets, and was brought about by the fact that it constituted a handy method of extracting from the dense oak forests lying to the east of the Baltic, in the territories behind the ports of Riga, Danzig, and Memel, the best of the timber. Wainscots were made by manual labour in the woods by means of first splitting the log with wedges, and then adzing the resultant halves, so as to provide an 8″ – 10″ face. In some cases, however, the round logs would be floated down the rivers in rafts, and the Wainscots manufactured at the actual port of shipment. The bulk of the oak shipped from the port of Memel came from Lithuania, Volhynia, and other districts in the immediate hinterland. But some of the more choice oak planks and staves came from the great forests growing between the Dniester and the Dnieper rivers.

From 1775 to the outbreak of the Napoleonic Wars the bulk of Wainscot logs reaching the British market came from Riga in the shape of billets about 14 ft. long, containing roughly 18–20 ft. cube per piece. They were commonly graded for export purposes into two classes known as " Crown " and " Brack." The term " Crown " Wainscot was a synonym for perfect quality in the British timber trade for many years down to the First World War. The " Brack " quality permitted just a few small knots. At the port of shipment a third quality was put on one side for local consumption. This early use of the term " Brack " as denoting a second quality is certainly very interesting. It no doubt dates from the time when only the " Crown " Wainscots would have been shipped, and the remainder ' bracked,' or placed on one side. In addition to the sources mentioned above, one principal place of origin for the Wainscots shipped from the port of Riga was the great province of the Ukraine. By the time trade was resumed on the conclusion of war in 1815 the great forests in the Government of Kiev were being exploited, and in consequence the size of the Wainscots rose to 22–24 ft. cube. Further, they were no longer sold by the piece, but were measured with a string, and the price charged according to their cubical feet contents.

At this early date Wainscot billets even reached the port of London from as far afield as Odessa, in the Black Sea. Wainscot logs from Memel were of larger dimensions, and so yielded boards of greater length and breadth, but the wood was considered by the eighteenth-century joiners and carpenters to be not so mellow, and also to carry less figure. Here is a small table showing the cost of Imported Memel Wainscot logs in the year 1826 :

Prime cost	57s. 3d.
Freight	11s. 1d.
Charges	2s. 0d.
Total, without duty	70s. 4d.
Duty	23s. 3d.
	93s. 7d.

A Mr James Hume, a Scots importer operating in the Baltic, was asked by the above-mentioned Select Committee, " What sort of timber are these Wainscot Logs ? " He replied as follows :

A species of Oak ; what is used in Churches ; and a great deal of it will be required in the new Houses of Parliament. It was also formerly almost exclusively used for boat-building ; but the Canada oak has superseded it for that purpose. The duty on mahogany was reduced from £3.1.6d. to £1.10s. per ton ; while the duty on wainscot still continues. There should be a reduction of 30s. a load upon it, if that is to continue to be imported.

Talking of public buildings, another witness before the Select Committee was asked his opinion of oak from the North American Continent, and replied as follows :

The American oak is a bad substitute for wainscot, as it is exceedingly liable to warp, and to change the form the joiner gave it, however long it may have been seasoned. Needy builders, who work for contract, sometimes use it, and call it wainscot ; and I know of one public building in which it has been introduced, and, I suppose, paid for under that name.

This is a very interesting piece of evidence, showing that imported Wainscot Oak was already being used in very large quantities in British joinery and panelling.

Another source of supply of Wainscots was Holland. But in this case the material came forward to the British market in the form of Wainscot boards, the logs being converted in sawmills driven by windmills, situated largely in the neighbourhood of the ports of Amsterdam and Rotterdam. The oak logs were brought down the Rhine to these ports, and came principally from the great forests of the Ardennes and the country lying between the rivers Moselle and Meuse. Thus the Dutch Wainscot boards were cut mostly to a standard size of 12′ long × 12″ wide × 1″ thick, and were consequently sold at so much the piece. In the 1780's there was a war between Great Britain and Holland, and for a time the importation of these Dutch Wainscots was suspended. However, means of resuming the trade were soon found. The Dutch merchants would make a nominal sale to neutral German firms at Emden, or alternatively ship it in Flemish vessels from the port of Ostend. Needless to say, in such circumstances the cost of freight rose from $1\frac{3}{4}d.$ to $7d.$ per ft. cube. It is obvious that the merchant communities in the seventeenth and eighteenth centuries did not have the same views on what constituted trading with the enemy as are now held in our twentieth-century wars. It is possible to make an excuse for the trading communities during these centuries, inasmuch as war in Europe was almost endemic, and no doubt traders felt that they were benefiting their customers by carrying on trade in almost any circumstances. For instance, it is well known that during the Napoleonic Wars, despite Napoleon's Continental System which forbade the export of European goods to England, considerable quantities of commodities, including timber, continued to reach the United Kingdom from ports of many Continental countries.

It is interesting that solid Wainscot logs were also imported from Holland, but the main complaint against these articles was that they were full of defects, so that solid Wainscots could not be imported from Holland with advantage. This was presumably due to the fact that the owners of the wind-driven sawmills naturally selected the best of the logs for conversion in their own mills.

It is interesting to learn from the Custom House Returns that Sierra Leone Oak, presumably the wood now known as Iroko, was being imported as early as 1800 in the shape of logs at a price of £8 5s. to £9 per load. The wood was being used in the Royal Dockyards, and is one more proof of the continual preoccupation of the Admiralty to procure enough reliable ship-building timber. It is no doubt the general opinion that the ships of the British Navy, poetically known as "the wooden walls of England," were mainly built entirely of English Oak, but in the period of great naval expansion caused by the Napoleonic Wars this was certainly not the fact. Danzig and Memel Oak was imported in considerable quantities to make up the shortage of the home article, and, in fact, for a number of reasons the Baltic Oak was preferred by the shipwrights. No wonder, when we are told that much of the Danzig Oak plank was imported in lengths of from 24′–60′ at a price of 4s. to 5s. per cubic foot. It was generally admitted, however, that the English Oak plank was more suitable for use at or above the water-mark, or 'whale-piece,' as it was called. The English timber was held to be more resistant to the alternative effects of wind and water, whereas many ships were entirely built of Danzig Oak below the water-line.

Apart from the oak reaching the British market from the great forest-lands to the east of the Baltic behind the ports of Danzig, Memel, Riga, and Königsberg, fresh areas for the supply of oak were developed in the middle of the eighteenth century in the territories of the Austria-Hungary Empire, particularly from the woodlands of the provinces of Slavonia and Croatia (now part of Jugoslavia). The first water sawmill to operate in these districts was erected in 1712 at Gorsky-Kotor, in Southern Croatia. The motive-power of this mill was changed to steam in 1830. The timber productions of Slavonia and Croatia were originally exported solely through the port of Venice. Round logs of American Oak were imported into the United Kingdom from the beginning of the eighteenth century. By 1850, however, a number of sawmills were erected in the United States for the large-scale production of sawn lumber.

The first shipment of American Oak lumber arrived in London in 1861; the wood was originally obtained from the virgin forests of Virginia, and here was produced the famous White Oak known to the trade as " Virginia Oak." Later the central and southern states of the U.S.A. became large suppliers of oak, and in due course the variety known as Red Oak reached the British market.

Japan and Manchuria were the last great oak-producing territories in the world to contribute their quota to the British market. It was not until the beginning of the twentieth century that this oak, in the form of square logs, first reached this country. Very soon an efficient sawmilling industry grew up in Japan, drawing its supplies from the Japanese isles and also the mainland of Manchuria. From 1910 onward large consignments of Japanese Oak lumber have reached the market of the United Kingdom, the flow being interrupted only by two World Wars.

CHAPTER XII

SAWMILLING

WOODWORKING machinery was set up in Holland, Germany, and Sweden as early as the fifteenth and sixteenth centuries. The earliest industrial sawmill is said to have been erected in Norway in 1530, while one was erected at Saadam, in Holland, in 1596. In England they were not introduced until much later; the pitsawyers felt that injury might be done to their trade and induced Parliament to prohibit them by legislation. The machines consisted of crude reciprocating saws set up in wooden frames and driven mainly by wind- or water-power, although in some cases an animal or even a man would be harnessed for motive-power to some kind of a wheel. The first circular saw was actually invented

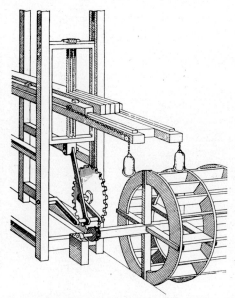

A Sixteenth-century Water-driven Norwegian Vertical Frame Saw

in Holland about the middle of the eighteenth century, but to start with was not a great success owing to the difficulty of tempering the teeth. In fact, it was not until the lapse of another hundred years that the circular saw really came into its own, as we shall see in the story of the U.S.A.

In the year 1555 an Ambassador of Queen Mary described a primitive vertical frame saw, which he had seen in operation when he was on a journey in the neighbourhood of Lyons, as follows :

> The Saw mill is driven with an upright wheel ; and the water that maketh it go is gathered whole into a narrow trough, which delivereth the same water to the wheel. This wheel hath a piece of timber put to the axle-tree end, like the handle of a broch, and fastened to the end of a saw, which being turned by the force of the water, hoisteth up and down the saw, that it continually eateth in, and the handle of the same is kept in a rigall of wood from swerving. Also the timber lieth as it were upon a ladder, which is brought by little and little to the saw with another vice.

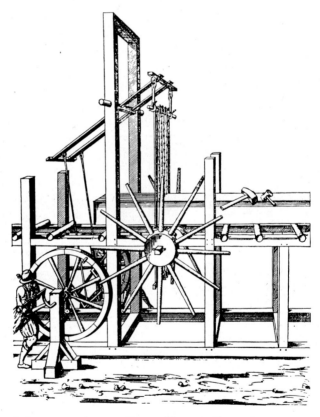

A Sixteenth-century Dutch Vertical Frame Saw, driven
by Man-power

By courtesy of the Timber Development Association, Ltd.

This machine, noted by the worthy Ambassador, or, perhaps, more likely by his Secretary, in one of his periodical reports to the Queen's Council, must be the forerunner of all vertical frame saws ! It is an interesting fact that after some years of comparative neglect in favour of the band-mill the vertical frame saw with many modern improvements is becoming increasingly popular even in countries like the U.S.A. and Canada, which hardly knew it earlier. This may well be due to the decreasing size of trees available to-day. The frame saw is ideal for converting small- to medium-sized logs.

Great Britain was backward in the adoption of mechanical plant for sawing wood. It was the custom for the Royal Society of Arts, established in 1754, to offer awards and prizes for details and plans of industrial machinery which the Society's Council felt would be of national advantage. Accordingly, the R.S.A. awarded a premium of £300 to one James Stanfield in 1761 for the plan of the first sawmill to be erected in England (Yorkshire). Mr Stanfield had gained his experience by seeing sawmills operating in both Norway and Sweden. He deposited the specifications for his sawmill with the R.S.A., and from these we learn that the driving-power was supplied by a water-wheel 18″ in diameter equipped with 25 steps or paddles. This water-wheel supplied the driving-power for three frame saws. The logs were carried on carriage frames, and a lead counterweight was employed to keep the saw in contact with the timber. It is interesting to note that the Society for American Colonists also paid Stanfield £60 for a model of his original mill. Subsequently Stanfield was introduced to a London timber merchant named Charles Dingley, and for him he designed and built a sawmill at Limehouse. This second sawmill was driven by wind-vanes, after the style of a windmill. Soon after its erection the building was attacked and set on fire by a mob of disgruntled pitsawyers who feared for their livelihood.

However, it survived, and, inspired no doubt by the above examples, Samuel Miller, a builder of Southampton, was granted in 1779 a patent for an improved sawmill machine. Miller's patent was No. 1152, and from this specification we can see that the machine was driven by a windmill, and that the machine was based on a new principle inasmuch as it was proposed to do the cutting by a number of circular saws mounted on a shaft.

The R.S.A. were not deterred by the disturbances arising out of the erection of these early sawmills, and continued to offer awards for plans of efficient sawmills, with the result that in the year 1782 they were proudly able to place the following statement in the report of their transactions for the year :

> Intimidated by a groundless suggestion of a pretended prohibitory Act of Parliament, this country submitted for many years to have timber cut into boards by the sawmills of Holland, and other foreign countries, till the Publick spirit, and the rewards of the Society interposing, prejudice was overcome and to the great gratitude and emolument both of the Publick and of the particular undertakers sawmills are now firmly established in England.

The sawmilling industry in Great Britain owed a great debt of gratitude to the Bentham Brothers. Samuel Bentham was Inspector-General of Naval Works, and in this capacity he was sent by the Government in 1779 on a tour of a number of European countries to investigate the state of woodworking and shipbuilding. After his return to England he invented the first planing machine for wood, and took out a patent for it in 1791. Samuel's brother, Jeremy Bentham, the famous writer on political economy, was also employed by the Government on the task of introducing industry into British prisons. The type of labour available being generally unskilled, he called upon his brother Samuel to help him devise machines that would replace the want of industrial skill in the prisoners. The great need was for woodworking machines, because timber was largely used in the prison workshops, being in those days the main structural material. Shipbuilders and carpenters, millwrights and engineers, all employed wood as the basis of their work. Arising out of these events, the two brothers entered into partnership, and on receiving considerable orders from the Government they turned the house of Jeremy Bentham, situate in Queen's Square Place, Westminster, into the first factory in this country solely devoted to the manufacture of woodcutting machinery. This was in the year 1794. Later additional accommodation was occupied at 19 York Street. It was not, however, until 1797 that the Admiralty in their turn decided to install a number of the Bentham machines in their dockyards at Portsmouth and Plymouth. The frames of these machines were made of heavy timbers bolted

together. Only the cutters and crude bearings were of metal.
The extent of the operations of the brothers Bentham may be
gauged from the fact that after an arbitration in 1813 the Government eventually settled with them for machinery furnished to
the dockyards and prisons for the sum of £20,000—a very considerable sum in those days. It was stated at this inquiry that
the machines saved nine-tenths of the labour, and that a table
could be made at one-half the expense.

The Benthams were joined in 1810 by a young man named
Brunel, known to history as Sir Marc Isambard Brunel, who
introduced a number of improvements into the circular saw so
as to turn it into a practical tool. For this he was granted two
patents, one in 1805 and one in 1808. He was awarded the sum
of £16,000 as a result of the above-mentioned arbitration. In
1807 Brunel took out a patent for his famous ship's block machinery. It may not be generally appreciated that in the days of
England's wooden walls a fully rigged frigate of the line was
equipped with some 1500 blocks, and that up to this time each
one of them was made entirely by hand. In the light of this
information the effect of the saving made by Brunel's machines
can be more exactly appreciated. Although Brunel was a clever
engineer, he did not have the actual practical knowledge to carry
out his ideas, and in his work he was joined by Henry Maudeslay,
who was an expert mechanic and a practical joiner. It is a fact
that in those days inventors and patentees very rarely supplied
methods or plans, but generally furnished merely a description
of their machinery, leaving it to others to build it. In fact,
very many of these early patents were never translated into
actual machinery at all. In 1803 Sir Samuel Bentham as their
Inspector-General advised the Admiralty to permit the erection
of steam-engines to drive his machines, and some were accordingly installed. By this time the dockyards were fitted with
crude machinery for sawing, planing, boring, tenoning, and
mortising. Apart from their elementary construction, it can
be seen that they had nearly all the principles found in modern
machines.

Another man who aided the development of sawmilling
machinery was Joseph Bramah, who in 1802 invented a planing
machine, which was later improved by Daniel. These early sawmilling machines were, indeed, roughly made and cumbersome in

operation, but owing to the colossal labour involved in sawing and machining by hand, even the most primitive power-driven saws were welcomed by timber merchants. On the evidence that has already been considered regarding the amount of sawn timber used in Great Britain, it is evident that up to the middle of the nineteenth century very large numbers of men must have been employed as pitsawyers both in the woods and in timber merchants' yards up and down the country. No doubt it was partly a seasonal occupation, many of the men being employed in agriculture in the summer, while they spent the winter in the woods.

Benjamin Cummins, of Schenectady, New York, made the first American circular saw in his blacksmith's shop at Bentville in the year 1814. He used the original tools of his craft, and produced a crude hand-forged saw with square mandrill holes. This Mr Cummins was a man of parts even for those early days of the fast-growing young Republic. He died in 1843, and here is an extract from his obituary :

> He was a first cousin to one of the Presidents of the United States ; a slave-owner in New York State ; a leading Mason, at whose table the very elect of the great state of New York feasted and drank freely of his choice liquors and wines ; a vessel owner on the North River before the days of steamboats ; a captain in the War of 1812, where, after having horses shot from under him, with one stroke of his sword he brought his superior officer to the ground for insult and because he was a traitor and coward and, after having been court-martialed, instead of having been shot he was appointed colonel in his place. He constructed a mile and a half of the Erie Canal through a bed of rock, and aided in the construction of the first ten miles of railroad, built in the United States.

The patent of an improved circular saw was applied for by Robert Eastman, of Brunswick, Maine, in 1824. Specifications for nine planing machines were patented in the U.S.A. before 1820, but it was William Woodworth, of New York State, who invented the first planing machine using feed rollers together with rotary cutters. This invention was violently resented by the carpenters and joiners—in fact, the sawmill at Poughkeepsie, where the first planing machine was installed, had to be watched day and night in case it should be set on fire by the opposition. Woodworth ultimately received 5000 dollars for his patent, which was bought by a syndicate who permitted only a limited number of planing machines in each district. In other words, timber could be planed only by machines licensed by them. The charge to a consumer was 7 dollars per 1000 feet, of which 3 dollars was paid to them in royalties. It was only after extreme pressure on Congress that this monopoly was finally broken down in 1865. A monster petition covering fifty feet in length was laid before Congress, and so ended the famous Woodworth monopoly. A tenoning machine was invented by Mr J. A. Fay in 1834 at Keene. Later he built a factory at Cincinnati for the production of woodworking machinery, which is still in busines s under the name of Fay and Egan.

Up to the time of the Universal Exhibition in Hyde Park in 1851, sponsored by Prince Albert, the manufacture of wood-working machines remained on a limited basis, and no great advances were made on the earlier technique. At this exhibi-tion not only was woodworking machinery from all over Europe on exhibit, but a number of American machines were to be seen. The bringing together of these various types seemed to have afforded a stimulus to engineers, and from thence onward there is an immediate advance in ideas, and fresh principles appear. These exhibitions focused the attention of engineers working in many different countries on their common problems and the steps which had been taken by their opposite numbers to solve them. In other words, they permitted a synthesis of sawmilling invention to take place. Generally speaking, this period marked the finish of what may be called the 'Heath Robinson' era of sawmill machinery. Up to then the woodworking machinery had been largely made of wood with clumsy, rickety framework. It is in the catalogues of these great exhibitions, however, that woodworking machinery begins to appear with cast-iron frame-work and substantial bases. The machines were often embellished with gilt and other scroll-work, giving them a typically Victorian appearance.

It is interesting to look through the nineteenth-century cata-logues of woodworking machinery and to note the early efforts of a number of firms still in existence either under the same name or by direct descent. For instance, Messrs Alan Ransome and

Co. of London had a considerable variety of machines in production by 1870. At the Exhibition of 1862, among others, the
following firms were exhibiting : Messrs Robinson and Sons
of Rochdale, McDowell and Sons of Glasgow, and Mr W. B.
Haigh of Oldham. From the United States Messrs S. A. Woods
of Boston were in production prior to 1870, and also the well-
known firms which figure in these early records, but which the
writer can no longer identify as being still in existence, are :
Messrs Richards of London, F. Arbey of Paris, Kelley of Philadelphia, and C. B. Rogers and Co. of New York.

At the time of the great expansion of the Middle West,
timber was the common building material, and batteries of gang
saws of simple design were used in large sawmills established at
such places as St Anthony, on the Mississippi, at the Falls of St
Croix, in Wisconsin, and Saginaw, in Michigan. A simple type
of frame saw much favoured in the U.S.A. to supply rough-sawn
lumber was the so-called " Mulay-Sawmill." This saw consisted in principle of an unstrained vertical saw mounted at the
bottom end on guides to which a connecting-rod was attached,
while the upper end of the saw was similarly mounted on guides
to a light cross-head. These guides could be so regulated in
regard to the size of the log that very little of the saw was exposed. The Mulay saw worked with a slow feed, and the
number of revolutions was from 300 to 400 per minute. The
makers, Messrs Chandler and Taylor of Indianapolis, claimed
that it cut smooth and even lumber, leaving no " stub shot,"
and would saw logs up to 4 ft. in diameter. It was further said
that it was portable, and could be re-erected on a new site in
two or three days by unskilled labour. In fact, so highly esteemed
was the lumber from this machine on account of the smoothness
and regular thicknesses that it commanded a superior price.

At the International Exhibition held in Paris in 1878 the
latest development of the gang saw was a machine which cut
two flitches or cants at one operation. The story of wholesale
lumber production is virtually the history of the invention
and the development of the band-mill. This idea was originally
patented as early as 1808 by William Newberry of London,
but owing to the difficulties of tensioning the saw, it was
not until the Paris Exhibition of 1855 that an actual working machine was placed on the market. The installation of the

MODERN DUPLE GANG SAW IN A BRITISH COLUMBIAN SAWMILL
By courtesy of Seaboard Lumber Sales, Canada.

first successful band-mill in the U.S.A. may be credited to Mr J. R. Hoffman, of Fort Wayne, Indiana, in the year 1870 ; while at about the same time Mr Van Pelt of New York is recorded as owning a large lumber-mill equipped with several bandsaws supplied by both Richards of London and Kelley of Philadelphia. The blades used were 60 ft. long and 5″ wide, with the saw

NEWBERRY'S ORIGINAL BAND-MILL, PATENTED IN 1808

running at a speed of some 4500 revolutions per minute. Necessity is said to be the mother of invention, and the necessity of the United States were the facts that they had large stands of virgin timber while the country needed vast quantities of lumber for the rapid development of their ever-growing cities, and at the same time there was a great shortage of labour. Many of the early band-mills were crude affairs made by the local smithy. The bandsaws themselves were hand-forged, unpolished, and often badly tempered. The sawmill carriages were frequently built of timber, with only the head-blocks and knees of cast-iron. The ancillary machines were small and crude, but they did the work. The side-edger would consist of a circular saw to which lumber would be fed on a very light, narrow table mounted on small rollers, which permitted the pushing of only one board at a time up to the saw. Slabs and edgings were cut into chunks for the furnace to heat the inevitable boiler by a swing saw. From these primitive installations grew the modern American lumber-mill, with its large vertical bandsaws, equipped with blades up to 12″ wide, and with its complementary system of hydraulic jacks, known as 'niggers,' for throwing the log into position and subsequently turning it as required by the sawyer.

By 1880 factory-made bandsaws were placed upon the market in the U.S.A. Messrs Sinker-Davis and Co.'s first band-saws had a wooden column and would cut 10,000 feet of poplar logs a day. Very soon this firm turned out an all-iron framework and produced a much improved model which they advertised as " The Gold Dust " Mill. Previously in all band-mills it had been found necessary to adjust the top or drive wheel in order to strain the saw so as to give the proper tension to the cutting-edge, and so prevent the saw from running off the wheel. Messrs Sinker-Davis's band-mill, however, provided an upper wheel with three adjustments which permitted the wheel to be set to any given pitch, and it had a saw of 40 ft. in length. In 1878 an International Exhibition was held in Paris at which a number of bandsaws were shown, including machines made by Messrs Weston and Co. of London and Messrs Arbey of Paris.

The problems connected with the resawing of lumber early occupied the attention of sawmill engineers. In the early days lumber was largely produced by original conversion to the thick-nesses approximating to its final use. This was so whether the board was converted by a pitsawyer or a primitive frame. Later on, however, as it became necessary to increase largely the pro-duction to meet the demands of industry, means were found by which the quantity of output was greatly increased by the prelim-inary sawing being done on primary conversion units in the shape of baulks and planks, the material being subsequently resawn into the appropriate thicknesses.

Resawing was first of all done on deal frames and circular saws. Sawing on deal frames, while accurate and economical, was slow, while the production from circular saws, although much greater in quantity, produced almost as much waste in the shape of saw-kerf and off-cuts as there was lumber. Consequently when considerable improvements in the design and operations of band saws took place the sawmill machinery producers in both the United Kingdom and the United States set

MODERN HORIZONTAL BAND-MILL WORKING IN A LONDON SAWMILL
By courtesy of John Wright and Sons (Veneers) Ltd.

about designing band saws that could be used for resawing, and were consequently known as band-resaws. When once perfected these had the great advantage not only of giving accurate sawing, but also, because they took a much thinner cut, of greatly reducing the saw-kerf, or waste. Band-resaws first came into operation at the commencement of the twentieth century, and by the end of World War I were quite extensively used. Progressive improvements have been continually made in their design, both in regard to accuracy of the cut and the quickening of the feed-rate. Band saws remain a popular class of machine to-day, and many are found both in large sawmills and in joinery works and furniture factories.

The original planing machines were simple, and all subsequent moulding was done by hand. In the year 1856 Messrs Powis James and Co. of London placed on the market a simple planing and moulding machine invented by their manager, Mr Henry Wilson. Later, at the International Exhibition of 1862, Messrs Robinson and Sons of Rochdale showed a new planing and moulding machine driven by a feed motion with four speeds. Shortly afterwards Messrs Alan Ransome and Co., Ltd, designed a combined moulding and planing machine with a number of independent cutter-blocks and four different rates of feed varying from 12 to 50 ft. per minute, thus enabling floorings, skirtings, and mouldings to be run in one operation. A great step forward in the design of fast-running moulding machines was the introduction of the cylindrical cutter-head. This was developed in England and Germany in the early part of the twentieth century, and shortly afterwards introduced into the United States by the Oliver Machine Company. At the same time as these inventions were taking place in the United Kingdom moulding machinery was produced in the United States by both Messrs J. A. Fay and Co. of Cincinnati and Messrs S. A. Woods of Boston ; while Sweden, represented, among others, by the famous firm of Bollinder, was early in the field with a moulding and matching machine with a feed-rate of some 600 ft. per minute. Planing machines were originally all of the carriage type—that is to say, the material to be planed was borne under the planing-knife by a carriage. This system made the rate of feed very slow, and the first great advance was made in this type of machinery when the principle of roller-feed was invented. This new principle automatically pushed up the rate of feed many times and vastly increased the output. One of the first planing machines fitted with roller-feed was shown by Mr Samuel Worssam of London at the Great Exhibition of 1851. At the same time Messrs C. B. Rogers and Co. and B. D. Whitney were working on the same principle in the United States. These early planing machines were all quite narrow, and a great step forward was made at the commencement of the twentieth century when large panel planers came into use, planing panels up to 42″ wide. These panels in mahogany and similar woods (mostly cut to $\frac{1}{2}$″ and $\frac{5}{8}$″) were part of the stock-in-trade of every timber merchant dealing with coachmakers and the railway companies. With regard to modern moulding and planing practice, the following quotation from a treatise on woodworking machines written by J. Richards in 1872 is illuminating :

> The operator in a planing mill must, or should, understand the whole theory of carpentry and joinery ; he should carry in his head by memory thousands of standard dimensions, with the names and catalogue numbers of catalogue mouldings of every form ; he must understand machinery fittings so as to direct and make repairs, and must besides be strong and healthy to stand the wear and anxiety incident to his calling.

The early woodworking machinery was driven by wind-, water-, animal-, and even man-power. Bentham in some cases employed primitive steam-engines to drive his woodworking machines, but it was not until the middle of the nineteenth century that really practical steam-engines came into use in sawmills. The engine was usually placed at one end of the mill so as to drive a big main shaft. When electric motors were first introduced into sawmills at the beginning of the twentieth century this complicated system of driving by means of main and subsidiary shafting was not at once changed, as one motor merely replaced the steam-engine formerly used. Very soon, however, it was found that an individual motor for each machine or a group of machines was much more efficient. This new practice did away with the complicated mass of shafting and belting. After World War I a further refinement of power-driving took place, inasmuch as in the case of log-sawing machinery it became general to provide motors for the separate purposes of operating the log-carriage and driving the saw, while in the case of high-speed moulding machines a motor would be harnessed to each cutter-block, with another for the feed. At one time it was fashionable to drive the individual cutter-block direct off the shaft of the motor, but this practice has now been largely abandoned in favour of transmitting the power by means of a short belt, known as a " V " belt, between the motor and the cutter-block. It has been found that this later technique lends itself to smoother running.

Type H.U. 12″ × 6″ Extra-heavy Four-side High-speed Planing and Moulding Machine, with Built-in Electric Motors on Each Cutter-head

By courtesy of Thomas White and Sons, Ltd., Paisley

It is a matter of some comment when it is realized how early the method of clearing sawmill shavings, chips, and dust by fans or blowers came into use, particularly in the United States. By 1870 at the latest an engineer of Boston, Mr B. F. Sturtevant, was planning and erecting extraction plants. These were operated very much on the same principle as to-day, a large induction fan being placed at some central point and connected up with pipes of either sheet-metal or wood to the various machines. Mr Sturtevant is the founder of the famous Sturtevant Engineering Co., Ltd, of London and New York.

Woodworking machinery has probably not developed as quickly and radically as that in the metal trade. This may be proof that the original principles adopted by the fathers of the sawmill engineering industry were thoroughly sound. Most progress has probably been made under the following three headings : safety in operation ; methods of driving ; speed of output. The early sawmilling machinery must have been very, very dangerous : practically no guards were provided, and the mills were a mass of unprotected shafting and belting. Nowadays direct motor drives have greatly cut down all this, and what is left is properly protected. Machinery guards have been so perfected that if properly used the chances of an accident are reduced to a minimum.

The speeding up of sawmill machinery is largely due to the following factors : high-speed motors ; frequency changers ; precision ball-bearings ; and special high-speed steels. Ball-bearings came into use in this country and Europe towards the end of the nineteenth century, but it was some years later before they appeared in the United States, which up to then had used mostly the older type bearings of Babbitt metal. With the coming of ball-bearings it became possible to invent bearings which would stand up to the greatly increased operating speeds demanded by modern machinery. Improved bearings alone, however, would not have enabled the modern high outputs to have been attained without the use also of high-speed steel in the manufacture of saws, planing-knives, and cutters. When it is realized that modern sawmilling machinery is expected to operate at speeds of 6000 to 7000 revolutions per minute, rising even to 9000 r.p.m. in the case of high-speed routers, French spindles, etc., it will be appreciated what advance has been made in less than a hundred years.

To-day it is the practice not only to use high-speed steel for the aforementioned purposes, but also to tip both the teeth of saws and the edges of cutters with Tungsten alloy " Stellite." Band-mills have been improved, and made even more labour-saving in two directions. Firstly, in the lighter machines a device has been perfected which enables the single operator to pre-set the thickness of his next cut while the log-carriage is travelling into position. Secondly, in the large American band-mills where previously three men were required to ride upon the carriage in order to operate the various devices for holding and turning the log, this operation with the aid of compressed air can now be performed by one man.

The necessity for keeping large modern plant clean if it is to work efficiently, not to say to meet the demands of the modern Factory Inspector, has led to very considerable improvements in the installations used for extracting chips, waste, and sawdust from woodworking machinery. It is common practice now-adays to inspect an up-to-date plant and to see practically no waste material lying on the machines or on the floor, the whole having been drawn away by powerful fan installations as soon as made.

CHAPTER XIII

THE CARPENTER

TIMBER was almost the sole building material of early England. Indeed, it was not until the coming of the Normans that even the nobles began to build themselves castles of stone. The Anglo-Saxon kings and their thegns feasted in halls of wood, seated on wooden benches and drinking from wooden vessels. To such an extent was this so that the Anglo-Saxon word denoting to build is 'timbrian,' from the root noun meaning timber. In these circumstances the carpenter was naturally a very important person in the community. In the Pipe Rolls and monkish records he is usually called the Carpentarius, but sometimes the term Domifex, from the Latin *domus*, a house is used. It was the carpenter who provided the carts (*carrectar*) for bringing the material to the site. He made the centres (*cintra*) for the arches and vault ribs of the great cathedrals and monasteries. He was the provider of the hoisting tackle. In the Patent Rolls of 1330 we find a reference to the cost of constructing a " wyndas," or machine for hoisting up materials to the upper storeys and roofs of buildings. The description is as follows :

> 2 iron rings to bind the heads of the axle, 2 iron rods for the hauka of the wyndas on which rods the trendels have to turn or rotate, and an iron band 3 feet long and 3 fingers broad to bind and strengthen the rod of the wyndas which is badly broken, with 18 spikyngs to fasten the band onto the rod.

The tasks of the King's carpenters at Windsor Castle were many and various. They must, indeed, have taxed the ingenuity of the craftsmen concerned. For instance, the Pipe Rolls of the Castle show that in 1236 Simon the King's Carpenter had to repair the kitchen with two twisted posts (evidently to support the great spit) and also to mend the gutter. In 1240 the same carpenter was given a beech-tree for making tables for the use of the cooks in the great kitchen. This is an example of the early date at which our forefathers began to use special timbers for certain purposes. The following January the Constable instructed Master Simon to make a covered alley from the kitchen to the Great Hall, no doubt for the purpose of assisting the scullions in presenting the King's victuals warm at the table. From the context it sounds as if the servants had quite a walk.

The following were some of the tasks carried out piece-work. The difference in the value of money as between then and now must be taken into account, but, even taking all this into consideration, the prices seem remarkably cheap :

To John Plestowe carpenter for making the carpentry of a certain chamber newly built in the office called " le Scaldynghous "................................... 2s. 6d.

To William Cokhull for making the carpentry of a certain enterclose beside the tower called " le Blaketour " for the protection of animals......................... 13s. 4d.

To John Coterel carpenter for making the carpentry of a certain chamber newly built in the office of the King's saltinghouse.. 20s.

To William Cokhull and John Coterel, carpenters, for making the carpentry of the stalls, altar, and vestry, together with the making of a certain window called gapier, for the dean and chapter celebrating divine service by reason of the frailty of the King's old chapel within the castle .... £10.6s.

In those days payment was frequently made in kind, and included in the total cost of £23 9s. 3d. for work done at St Swithin's Priory, Winchester, was a sum of £6 to cover food for the workmen, which included 8 quarters of wheat, 48 carcasses of bacon, 21 cheeses, 6 casks of cider, with the sum of 15s. 6d. for meat and bread generally.

It will be noticed that in early medieval times carpenters and joiners were almost invariably paid only for the work done, the oak and other timbers usually being supplied by their employers, whether bishops, abbots, or barons. In the year 1392, however, one William Wright of Ripon was paid 12d. for oak timbers required to repair the towers of Ripon Minster. Later he was paid 18s. 7d. for making a door in the Choir, including the supply of " bords " for the work, while in 1409 at the same Minster he was paid 18d. for timber for making a locker, and a further 18d. for oak for a door behind the organ. The wages scheduled may seem to us small, but the cost of living was extremely low in medieval times, and no doubt they provided for a rude sufficiency. In the Exeter Fabric Rolls, Master Walter, a carpenter, in 1300, is shown as being paid 2s. 3d. per week, and another carpenter 2s. 1d., while a William de Trene in the year 1284 held the appointment of carpenter in the King's Houses in Ireland at a wage of a shilling a day and 40s. per annum for his clothes. In 1375 Hugh Herland was appointed to the "Disposal of the King's Works touching the art or mistery of carpentry" at the Tower of London and Westminster, with a shilling a day for his salary and "a winter robe yearly of the suit of the Esquires of the Household or such sum as the Esquires take therefor."

Also, in 1396, the same Hugh Herland was granted for life a little house at Westminster which he had used as a workshop and where he kept his tools. A shilling a day seems to have been top money, because Master Burnell, the King's Carpenter, is to be found working at Windsor Castle between 1333 and 1335 at 9d. a day, while in the year 1403 William Wyse, also a carpenter at Windsor Castle, was paid only 6d. per day, with a new suit of clothes every year. As mentioned above, sometimes carpenters were not only paid money, but also given food and lodging, their wages being reduced accordingly. The following is taken from a Petition during the reign of King Henry VI in 1443 :

> A Maister Tyler or rough-Mason and meen Carpenter and other Artificers concernyng beldyng by the day iijd. [3d.] with mete and drynk and without mete and drynk iiij½d. [4½d.]

Mention was made earlier of the low cost of living, and it will be seen here that the value of a working man's food and drink was computed at the sum of 1½d. per diem.

As mentioned earlier, in medieval days the carpenter was a very important personage in the community. Indeed, the King's Carpenter was also in effect Master of the Royal Ordinance. Before the invention of gunpowder the only weapons of offence against castle keeps and walls were a number of machines based on the sling principle and constructed of heavy timbers. An entry in the Windsor Pipe Rolls shows that on October 22, 1224, the King ordered five marks to be paid " to Master Jordan our

A THIRTEENTH-CENTURY CASTLE, SHOWING SIEGE OPERATIONS IN PROGRESS
Note the big trebuchet in the foreground.
From " A History of Everyday Things in England," vol. 1, by M. and C. H. B. Quennell (Batsford).

Carpenter who made our trebuchet at Dover." Previously the
Sheriff of Kent had been directed to afford facilities for the car-
riage to Dover of the timbers for making the said trebuchet.
While on November 9 of the same year the Sheriffs of London

were ordered to send to Dover by water eight brass wheels for the same. The King's trebuchet at Dover must have been a formidable machine, because the making of it occupied Master Jordan for no less than three years. In 1225 he is drawing timber from the forest of Oddiham for this purpose, and on June 8, 1226, there is the following entry : "That 3 marks in the part payment of his livery be paid to Master Jordan the Carpenter making our trebuchet," with further sums for his livery in July 1227.

The trebuchet was in principle a sling of enormous size made of heavy timbers. Its motive-power was derived from counter-poises and twisted hides. The scale of the machine may be estimated from the fact that it would sling stones—or, rather, rocks—up to a weight of half a ton. Its purpose, of course, was to batter breaches in the stone walls of the castles and towers, which, apart from this method of attack, could be subdued only by starvation. Such was its effect that in 1236 the King subdued the rebellious barons in Berkhamsted Castle in less than a fort-night.

The medieval carpenter used an astonishing variety of tools in carrying out his work. Among other authorities we are in-debted to Mr Francis B. Andrews, in his book *The Mediæval Builder and his Methods*, for the following information. A number of various kinds of saws were in use. There was the twortsaw or cross-cut saw used for cross-cutting logs and planks, together with a smaller and widely bladed saw called a " handsegh." It is interesting that this latter anticipated modern practice by having a curved cutting-edge. Pitsawing was done by a variety of saws known generally as " whip-sawes." They were primitive, narrow-bladed tools set in a frame, with one man pulling from above and the other pushing from below.

The logs or timber to be sawn were either placed over a pit or held on trestles. An assortment of axes were in use, such as the " dolabrum," a broad axe used for tree-felling and other heavy work ; the " securis," a small axe, and the " addice," or adze, which was a general utility tool used not only for felling and clearing, but also for rough-finishing the great mass of half-timbered work used in house construction. In the old Pipe Rolls chisels as a class are generally denoted by the Latin term " celtæ." Specialization in their design had already been carried to a considerable degree. There were " gougs," or gouges, which were used for their modern purposes, including a " thykstyll-goug," which may have been in the nature of an auger. Also there was an instrument called a " dryvelle," used for half-mouldings and rebating. The plane, known as a " planetorium " or " leviga," was much like its modern counterpart, the blade being fixed with a wedge in a block of wood, with a grip for the hand at the top. Braces were known as " wymbylls," and the large ones had chest-rests. Pincers were in common use, and were known as " forcipes." In medieval times there were, of course, no metal pipes, and the boring of pipes of a primitive nature formed a considerable part of the carpenter's work. This task was performed by means of long augers known by their Latin terms " terebellum " or " furfurculum."

In a picture of the building of the Ark from the Bedford Book of Hours we see a number of carpenters at work. One uses a handsaw with the curved blade mentioned above. Another is occupied with a plane, and a third with an auger. Lying on the ground are various carpenter's tools, such as a brace, a mallet, a chisel, and a whipsaw. One labourer is shown with a heavy axe.

It has to be borne in mind that in medieval times the term carpenter denoted not only the working craftsman, but also a master carpenter in the modern sense of the owner of a joinery works capable of carrying out the contract for building a house or the fitting up of a hall. In Lincoln there is existing an agreement dated the year 1316 between Master Roger de Leghton, Carpenter, and Sir John de Sandale, stating that Roger undertakes to construct two wings for Sir John's mansion at Boston ; that on the north side to be 136 ft. in length and 16 ft. in breadth ; the other on the south side to be 185 ft. long and 15 ft. wide. For this work Master Roger is to find the timber for the great beams (*maerem*) and the posts for the uprights, which are to be 14 ft. long and 12 in. square. Also there is to be supplied all the other timber and fittings for the buildings, including apparently the fitting of cupboards (gardrobes). Sir John de Sandale agreed with Master Roger to pay him for this work the sum of £37 in all ; the money to be paid in instalments : £10 at Easter, £10 at the Purification of the Blessed Virgin Mary, and the remainder when the work was completed. An indenture for the erection of a house in High Street, Bristol, is preserved. It was dated 1472, and agreed as follows :

> This indenture made between Alice Chester of Bristol, widow, sometime the wife of Harry Chester of Bristol, draper, on the one party, and Stephen Morgan of Bristol, Carpenter, on the other party, Witnesses, that the said Stephen hath covenanted with the same Alice and him bindeth by these presents to make well, workmanly, and surely of good timber and boards a new House in the High Street of Bristol, with floors, windows, doors, and partitions and all other things of timber work belonging to the same house except laths and lattices, which said new house shall be set between the tenement called the Bull on one party, and the tenement in which one John, a Cordviser[1] now dwelleth in, on the other party, containing in length 19 feet and 5 inches of size and in wideness 10 feet and 4 inches ; and the said Stephen shall make in the said shop, a hall above the same with an oriel, a chamber above that by the feast of the Annunciation of our Lady next coming for which house so to be made by the same Stephen the said Alice granteth and her bindeth by this present to payments the said Stephen 6L.18s.4d. sterling, that is to say at the feast of the Nativity of our Lord next coming 3L. at the flooring of the said house 38s.4d. and at the end of the same work 40s. Also it is accorded that it shall be lawful to the same Stephen to have and to take as his own all the old timber of the said old house without any gainsaying of the same Alice or any other for her or in her name. In witness thereof the parties aforesaid to these indentures interchangeably have set their seals. Given the 17th day of the month of November, in the 12th. year in the reign of King Edward the fourth.

It is a very vexed question as to how the great cathedrals and halls, etc., of medieval times were planned and designed. This applies equally to structures of stone and timber. Many theories, some based on remarkably little evidence, have been put forward. What contemporary evidence there is seems to show that in many cases the master carpenter or master mason, as the case might be, took the whole responsibility for the planning and conduct of the work. The history of the roofing of Westminster Hall in the latter half of the fourteenth century, as compiled in a record issued by H.M. Office of Works, gives the various persons in charge of the work with the responsibility for each

[1] Cordwainer or shoemaker.

BUILDING THE ARK

From the Bedford Book of Hours (*c.* 1423). Note the medieval carpenters at work.
British Museum.

THE FAMOUS HAMMER-BEAM ROOF OF WESTMINSTER HALL
By courtesy of the Parker Gallery, 2 Albemarle Street, London, W.1.

part clearly set out. For instance, while the stone-work of the
actual Hall itself was designed by Yevele, the planning of the
wonderful roof was the work of Master Hugh Herland, the
King's Carpenter. As a sort of general overseer, one John

Godmeston, a Clerk in Holy Orders, was appointed by the King to put the work in hand, with the following mandate :

> To cause the Great Hall in the Palace of Westminster to be repaired, taking the necessary masons, carpenters and labourers, wherever found, except in the fee of the Church, with power to arrest and imprison contrariants until further order, and also to take stone, timber, tiles and other materials and carriage for the same at the King's charges and to sell branches, bark and other remnants of trees. . . accounting for the monies as received and receiving in that office wages and fees at the discretion of the Treasurer of England.

Much of the oak for the Palace of Westminster built at the end of the fourteenth century for King Richard II was procured from woods near Farnham, in Surrey, where the trees were not only felled, but also wrought into the staunch timbers required for the roof of the Great Hall and other rooms. In 1395 an order was made for thirty strong " waynes " to convey the timbers from Farnham to Kingston, from which place they were brought down the river Thames to Westminster. It is interesting that Hugh Herland, Chief Carpenter Controller of the work, was given on October 17, 1397 :

> All the croppings and coppices which lay cut and remaining over in the wood near Kyngeston-oun-Thames.

While on July 14, 1360, William Herland, another member of the famous family, was given a receipt for a sum of £23 3s. 3¾d., for which he had made himself responsible by reason of " his industry about the making of stalls in the King's Chapel of Westminster, the sale of the wood of Reyndon, and of the lop and cropping of divers Oakes bought for the King's use and by him sold." The evidence of the chain of responsibility for the maintenance of the fabric of Windsor Castle as shown by the thirteenth-century Pipe Rolls is none too clear. In the year 1247 the Custodes were one John Silvester and Master Simon the Carpenter. In 1255 the Custodes of important works in the Castle were Master John of Gloucester, the King's Mason, and Alexander, the King's Carpenter. On January 14, 1257, this Alexander was appointed, by patent, master of all the King's works of carpentry, being the first holder of this new office ; he received furred robes twice a year in addition to his fees, which the King had already ordered to be doubled when Alexander was travelling on official business.   For the next ten years he was chief carpenter of the works at Westminster Abbey ;   in 1259 he was also in charge of work at the Palace, and in 1260 he is mentioned as owning property in Knightsbridge.   He died in or about 1269.   Master Alexander was a witness to many charters dated at Westminster between 1246 and 1269, while his son Henry made grants of houses and lands there which he had inherited from his father.   One of Alexander's most important works has survived—namely, the timber roof of Henry III's work at Westminster Abbey ;   the original timbers in the form of scissors trusses still stand, though much obscured by later strengthening pieces.

Another famous medieval master carpenter was Humphrey Coke, who was in his heyday at the end of the fifteenth century. His career is very interesting as showing the very varied nature of the duties of a master carpenter in medieval days, and also the responsibilities these men were called upon to assume.   In 1496 Humphrey Coke was appointed a member of a Commission to draft carpenters and labourers for the royal work in the North. In 1510 he was performing a duty which nowadays would be performed by an architect, and was paid 6s. 8d. for drawing the plan for the new cloisters at Eton College.   Again we find him drawing a design for the timber hall roof of Brasenose Hall, Oxford.   In the year 1519 he was given the office of the King's chief carpenter, with a retaining fee of 12d. a day.   This office he held until his death.   It is interesting that in this capacity in 1520 he worked with one William Vertue, the King's Mason, to draw up the plans for the famous occasion of the Field of the Cloth of Gold, when King Henry VIII met King Francis I of France.   We are glad to note that in return for all his hard work Humphrey Coke found time and opportunity to attend to his own personal affairs.   We find him making the following purchase :

> The messuage called the Cristofer, one Close, syx litill tenements and syx gardeyns in the parishe of Seynt Martyns in the Fields.

from Robert Chesman of Kentish Town.   Later he took a lease of the adjoining property from the Abbot of Westminster, including a gate-house.

The indenture between Arbury Priory and Thomas Stafford, carpenter, also shows admirably the wide scope of the medieval carpenter's duties, which, it will be seen, also cover many activities now carried out by timber merchants, sawmillers, and other

A ROYAL PERSONAGE GIVING INSTRUCTIONS TO THE KING'S CARPENTER
Fifteenth-century miniature.

traders. Thomas Stafford, described in the indenture as a carpenter, was retained to serve " the convent in the mistery and crafte of carpentry duryng the lyfe naturell of the seid Thomas." Stafford was to work " to the best avayle and profyte of the seid Priour and Couent as in chosyng, fellyng, squaryng of tymbre, framyng, reasyng, makyng and fynysshyng of houses and other such werks " as he should be ordered to do " that longeth or perteyneth a carpenter to do and make after his powre and cunnyng." He was to be paid £1 6s. 8d. a year " as long as he is myghty in body and abile to worche as a carpenter ought to doo . . . which he hath taken of the seid priour and Couent by copye of Court Roll which house lieth in Lutmanysend." The rent of this house, 13s. 4d. a year, was to count as part of his stipend, the other 13s. 4d. being paid in ready money quarterly. Stafford was also to take " mete and drynke dayly duryng the seid terme suche and in like forme as the hed yomen in the seid priory shall dayly haue and be serued and also barbour and launder wekely as the couent wekely ther haue," and yearly " iij brode yerds of wollen clothe for his gowne " as the said head yeomen wear.

The manner in which the building owner conveyed his wishes as to the style and design of the work varied considerably. Sometimes the master carpenter would simply be told to reproduce the style of roof found on an existing building in another

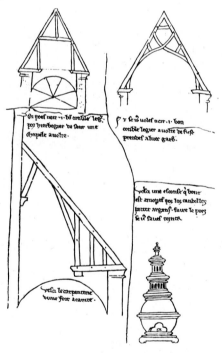

part of the country, or even abroad. Alternatively directions might be given as to the owner's general requirements, and a contract drawn up stating the dimensions of the building, together with reference to the positions of the various rooms, windows, doors, fireplaces, etc. There do not seem, however, to have been any plans as understood by modern architects. Having received his instructions from the owner, the master carpenter would then prepare certain rough drawings for the guidance of the workmen he employed, but these

A MASTER CARPENTER'S ROUGH SKETCHES, WITH
INSTRUCTIONS IN MONKISH LATIN

drawings and sketches would have been made on the job, possibly on wooden boards. These contracts are purely between the owner and the master carpenter. They contain no evidence that any third person had been called in either to design the work or to supervise its execution. The following piece-work contract for joinery, *c.* 1580, illustrates the method of the period :

> Christopher Saydgfeld hath taken by contract the parlour floor at the upper end of the hall perfectly to finish and lay ; to make and set up the portal workmanly to the height in every respect and to seal the same parlour round about with French panel four foot and ten inches high according to the pattern drawn for the same with base and arketrave [architrave] and to set a cornish [cornice] upon the top of the floor four inches in breadth downward or more and to make a portal of the same French panel to the height of the floor to be set up and workmanly finished in every respect and to make for the top of the same arketrave frisse [frieze] and cornice and two doors one for the portal and the other for the little wainscot chamber and make steapts [steps] that fall into the portal ; and on the steps for the window ; and to make two doors and hang the same for the turret at the bridge end ; the one to be hung up to shut and the other to stand a cuberd [cupboard] at the great chamber doors and hang the same for the turret at the bridge shall think fit ; for the doing thereof to have in money £8.13s.4. with meat drink and lodging for himself and his folks, tembr. naylles, glew [timber, nails, glue] and ten groats to buy him candles.

A little earlier we have the record of a carpenter complaining to Henry VII that whereas His Majesty had seen beforehand a picture of the roof of the Great Hall at Woodstock, and had approved it, the plans had subsequently been altered to the said carpenter's detriment. On the other hand, it is uncertain whether in some contexts the word plan does not convey the meaning of an actual model. Indeed, Sir Henry Wootton in 1624, in the time of James I, gives strict instructions as to how the building owner should set about carrying out his intentions :

> First, therefore, Let no man that intendeth to build, settle his Fancie upon a draught of the Worke in paper, how exactly soever measured, or neatly set off in perspective ; And much lesse upon a bare Plan thereof, as they call the Schiographia or Ground lines ; without a Modell or Type of the whole Structure, and of every parcell and Partition in Plastboard or Wood.

In conclusion, it may be said that the evidence seems to point to the fact that both the medieval master carpenter and the master builder undertook duties which nowadays would normally be considered functions of either the architect or the surveyor. Undoubtedly many buildings owed their design to being either copies of existing structures or by reason of the fact that, having viewed an existing structure, the master carpenter would take it for his design, plus such improvements and alterations as seemed to him to be good.   Thus a continual evolution of building practice took place by, one might almost say, process of trial and error.   Also, no doubt, considerable use was made of models, very rough in many cases, which were thrown away as soon as they had served their purpose.

The following entry of carpenter's work for the year 1534, apart from its intrinsic interest, is a fine example of the development which led to our modern spelling, and should please any schoolboy struggling with his first grammar :

> Carpenters.   Workyng as well uppon the borying and ffynssh-ying the wheell of the great well with Reparying and mending a Dore ffor the Coverying of the same as also makying a new leved Dore and a Wykett [wicket] in the same ffor the great Kechyn [kitchen] with a ffoldyng Dresser uppon the said Wykett to sett mette uppon at the serves tyme and also Repayring and mendyng not only the Rouffe [roof] of the Chambre where Patche the Kynges fowle [fool] Dyd lye but also the flower [floor] of the chambre.

The Carpenters' Company stands high among the leading Livery Companies of London.   It has a most interesting history. The Carpenters' Hall was a fine building standing at the junction of London Wall and Throgmorton Avenue.   It will be remembered with pleasure by many, but unfortunately, like many other fine City Halls, it was destroyed during the blitz in 1941.   The building of the Hall was actually commenced in 1429, and completed over a term of years.   From the accounts it can be gathered that the parlour was built in 1500, while the same records show that the Company had a fine garden and lavished money on it to make it beautiful.   Here were vines, fruit-trees, and rose-gardens, together with a sundial and a bowling alley for the recreation of the carpenters in their hours of leisure.   The first charter was actually granted to the Carpenters' Company by

Edward IV in the year 1477, but no doubt they had existed as a guild for a considerable period before the building of their hall. The poet Chaucer (born about 1340) can be quoted in support of this contention, for the following verse is found in the Prologue to *The Canterbury Tales* :

> An Haberdasher and a Carpenter,
> A Webbe, a Deyer, and a Tapiser,
> Were alle yclothed in a livere
> Of a solempne and grete fraternitie.

The medieval guilds, besides regulating wages and terms of work, which will be referred to later, fulfilled a number of other functions, among which were the making of suitable arrangements for the funerals of their members, which were celebrated with considerable ceremony, the livery members marching in procession behind the hearse. The great Livery Companies also played their part in the City's ceremonies and pageants. It was customary to divide the ' show ' among the various Companies, each mounting its tableau on a great wane, or wagon, which was drawn through the streets by a team of lusty horses. The following description of a religious pageant in the year 1450 shows the organization well. The following tableaux were presented :

1. The Creation of the World, by the mercers, drapers and haberdashers.
2. Paradise, by the grocers and raffemen.
3. " Helle Carte," by the glaziers, stainers, scriveners, parchemyners and carpenters.
4. Abel and Cain, by the shearmen, fullers, masons and limeburners.
5. " Noyse shipp " [Noah's Ark], by the bakers, brewers, innkeepers, cooks, millers, vintners and coopers.
6. Abraham and Isaac, by the tailors, broderers, the reders and tylers.

As a matter of comment, it will be noticed that while Paradise was entrusted to the grocers, it was the carpenters who took charge of the " Helle Carte " !

It has been said that by the fifteenth century the Carpenters' Livery in the City of London was so completely in control of the building industry that their licence had to be obtained to put up a wooden house, a shed, or even a pen for swans. On the other hand, it was the Livery's duty to see that the buildings

which they had licensed were properly built. In 1543 a house
was built for Mr Cowper by the two carpenters Thomas Sherman
and William Becham. Shortly afterwards it fell down owing to
defective work, and the two carpenters concerned had to share
the cost of its being properly rebuilt " as well for ther own
honystie as the honystie of the crafte." The Livery Companies
were concerned with pay and conditions of work. In theory at
any rate, no tradesmen, in the sense of a carpenter, mason, joiner,
etc., could work at his trade unless he either was a member of
the appropriate guild of the town in which he lived or alternatively was apprenticed to such a member. It is interesting that
after the Great Fire of London in 1666, when the necessity of
attracting craftsmen at all costs to the City was urgent, it was
found necessary to insert this clause in an Act of Parliament :

> All carpenters, bricklayers, masons, plasterers, joiners, and other
> artificers, workmen and labourers to be employed in the said build-
> ings, who are not freemen of the said City [of London] shall for
> the space of seven years next ensuing, and for so long time after
> as until the said buildings shall be fully finished, have and enjoy
> such liberty of working, and being set to work in the said building,
> as the freemen of the City of the same trades and professions have
> and ought to enjoy ; Any usage or custom of the City to the con-
> trary notwithstanding. And that such artificers as aforesaid, which
> for the space of seven years shall have wrought in the rebuilding of
> the City in their respective arts, shall from and after the said seven
> years have and enjoy the same liberty to work as freemen of the
> said City for and during their natural lives.

At the beginning of this chapter it was stated that timber was
literally the only building material available in the early days
of our island history. When we recollect that this state of
affairs lasted right down to the time of the Great Fire of London
in the cities and towns, and even longer in the countryside,
we can well appreciate why the carpenter's trade was such a
flourishing business, and the Carpenters' Company a very
powerful and important Corporation for many centuries.

In addition to regulating the wages and terms of employment
of their members, the Carpenters' Livery Company had other
important duties laid upon them by the Lord Mayor and Corporation of the City of London. Down to the passing of the first
Building Act in the year 1774 many of the duties now performed

by the City Surveyor were carried out by official "Viewers," senior members of the Guilds nominated by the Aldermen. To show the importance attached to their duties we append herewith the form of oath framed in the reign of Queen Elizabeth I :

The Othe of the Viewers
Maister Wardens of Masons
and Carpenters

Ye shall sweare that ye shall truly present from tyme to tyme to the Maior and Aldermen of this Citty for the tyme being, or to the Chamberleyne All such buildinge and Purprestures as ye shall fynd sett or made vpon any parte of the comon grounde of the said Citty. And from henceforth ye shall not make nor suffer to your knowledge to be made any newe building in any place within the liberty of this Citty, But ye shall the same shewe vnto the said Maior and Aldermen or Chamberleyne for the tyme being to th'entent that reformation thereof may be had. And also ye shall truly and indifferently search all manner of noysaunces, buildinge and edifyinge betweene party and party, when he shalbe charged by the Maior of the Cittie of London soe to doe, without any favor shewing to any party, And true reporte make to the said Maior for the tyme being vpon the premisses. And thus ye shall doe as Gold helpe you.

By the end of the seventeenth century the Aldermen, no doubt influenced by the increasing number of brick buildings, tended to nominate master masons as "Viewers," to the great annoyance of the Carpenters' Company. However, in point of fact the last official "Viewer" was a master carpenter, John Norris, who was appointed in the year 1737.

The election of the Master and Wardens was a serious affair, and took place annually in the summer. Here are the details of the ceremony laid down in advance by the Court for June 6, 1738 :

Directions for the Election of Master & Wardens of the Worshipful Company of Carpenters.

1st The Old Master & Wardens to walk once round the Hall with the Musick & Cupbearers.

Then the Old Master & Wardens to Crown the New Master & Wardens & to drink to each other.

Then the New Master & Wardens to walk once round the Hall with the Musick & Cupbearers as before.

N.B. To call the 4 Junr Livery Men to be Cupbearers.

In medieval days the Court or Council of the Carpenters' Company would meet and transact their business at breakfast, about eight o'clock in the morning ! In Elizabethan days it was 11 A.M., over a cup of wine ; at the Regency period the Council met for business at one o'clock, and dined in state at half-past three ; by the time of Queen Victoria and Prince Albert the Carpenters were dining at the then fashionable hour of 6 P.M. To-day their annual Livery Dinner is set for 7.30 P.M., nearly twelve hours later than the original breakfast meeting at 8 A.M., but then the medieval Masters and Wardens were working carpenters, and after their Court had a day's work in front of them !

From the middle of the nineteenth century the duties of the Court of the Carpenters' Company have largely consisted in the management of property and charitable gifts, the admission of Freemen, and, last but by no means least, the dispensing of their traditional hospitality. Now many of their early and essential duties both to members of their craft and the outside world have been taken from them by Government inspectors on the one hand and Trade Union officials on the other. However, there is one remaining task that the Carpenters' Company still pursue with unflagging energy, and that is the thorough technical education of young apprentices in their craft that is so necessary if British carpentry and joinery are to hold their own in the competitive world of the twentieth century.

CHAPTER XIV

TIMBER HOUSES AND HALLS

IT is proposed in this chapter to take a glance at the story of the development of timber houses and other structures throughout the ages. But first let us look at the oldest wooden building standing in the world to-day. It is the Horiuji Temple in Japan, built in A.D. 607 by the Crown Prince Shotoku at the order of the Empress Suiko. It is built of cypress wood which had been split by wedges, thus allowing the beautiful grain to be shown in the natural manner. The various buildings that stand in the precincts of the Buddhist Temple have been carefully restored from time to time, but nevertheless enough of the original woodwork and wonderful carving is left to give the visitor the feel of the genius of the ancient Japanese carpenters and wood-carvers.

It is fascinating to meditate that wood, the material which housed our neolithic forefathers, continues more than to hold its own in this twentieth-century age of jet planes and atomic research. In fact, such are the advances of wood technology that the demand for timber as a basic housing material is far greater in the twentieth century than it was in the preceding 200 years. Archæological research makes it clear that wood in some form or other was among the earliest of building materials. The excavation of the Lake Village at Glastonbury, which dates from about 350 B.C., shows that heavy timbers were first embedded in the marsh as a foundation. When this had sunk beneath the wet clay, huts were constructed by sinking vertical posts into the clay until they reached the sunken timbers. A substantial centre pole carried the roofs, and the lighter posts on the circumference were interlaced with wattle daubed with mud, so as to make a roof wall. The whole structure probably had the appearance of an African hut of the beehive type. A hearth for the fire was constructed in the middle of the hut, and the smoke escaped through a hole in the roof against the centre pole.

An Iron Age farm inhabited *circa* 300 B.C. has been excavated and reconstructed at Little Woodbury, Wiltshire. The reconstruction shows to the visitor a large circular hut constructed with stout posts and having four higher poles set in a square in the middle, which contained the fire-hearth. This also served to give the necessary pitch to the roof, which is shown as roughly thatched with reeds and rushes. The whole is enclosed in a much larger pallisade, and the area contained therein no doubt served as a yard for keeping the domesticated animals. It is fascinating to note that Mr Piggott, in the *Architects' Journal*, made a good case for presuming that the circle of wooden post-holes at Woodhenge is the remains of a large timber structure in the form of a hut partly roofed, the centre being left open to the sky.

While the Romans in their settled towns were great builders in brick and stone, there is considerable evidence that many of the early Roman villas and farmhouses in the southern part of Britain were largely built of timber. This has been proved by the nature of the stone and brick foundations, which in some cases bear traces of wooden posts and the markings of wattle walls. Even in the towns it is thought that in the case of many of the lesser houses the upper storey was certainly constructed of timber, filled in with some kind of a plaster. The Romans left the country for the last time in the early part of the fifth century, and the exact fate of their cities and towns is still a matter for research among archæologists. It is a reasonable assumption that while the Roman cities, towns, and luxurious villas fell into gradual decay, the large native population continued to live in their wooden farmhouses and huts much as they had done since the Celtic immigration, which took place from about 500 B.C. onward.

It is, therefore, to the arrival of the Saxon invaders that we must look for the new impulse in building construction, and timber buildings in particular. The key to Anglo-Saxon building work is afforded by the fact that the Anglo-Saxon word to build is 'timbrian,' which comes from the same root word as 'timber' or 'wood,' while the builder of the house was named the 'tre-owwyrhta,' or carpenter. The number of stone buildings was very few compared with those of wood, wood being always preferred to stone because of the heavy cost of transporting and working the latter. Indeed, it was not until relations were opened with the French and Norman territories across the

Reconstruction of an Iron Age Farmhouse at Little Woodbury, Wiltshire

Crown copyright reserved.

Channel in the tenth century that any form of stone building was attempted. The Saxons who settled in this country were a farming community under the rule of a loose confederation of chiefs, some of whom by extending their spheres of influence raised themselves in stature to earls and counts. As these local chiefs increased in power and enlarged their holdings of land into counties or earldoms, they were accustomed to build simple wooden halls for themselves in various parts of their domains, so that they could move about from place to place and supervise their territories. From various codes of Saxon and Welsh laws regarding building, together with the old chronicles of the Venerable Bede and others, we have some indication as to how these " King's Halls " were constructed. They were oblong structures based on parallel rows of wooden uprights, and of no great width. The open hearth was usually situated in the middle, so as to divide the hall into two sections, the upper part for the King and his officials and the lower part for his men-at-arms and followers. The door was generally placed in the middle opposite the hearth. Later on, as in the case of the more prosperous farms, side-aisles were added in which the common people slept at night, leaving the main body of the hall free for eating, drinking, and simple merry-making.

In Miss Hope Muntz's story *The Golden Warrior* we have an account of a more elaborate timber hall belonging to Earl Godwin, the father of King Harold. This is said to have been gilded and ornately carved over the porch and gables, so that it caught the rays of the sun. The long hearth for the great fire was in the middle of the hall, while the Earl's high seat stood in front of the north wall, and was said to have been long enough to seat six principal guests. Over it was a scarlet canopy, and on festival occasions the hall was hung with tapestries of red, purple, and blue, ornamented with gold. These simple timber halls or hunting-lodges persisted in Britain long after the Norman Conquest. In the Boldon Book of 1183 a description is given of a hunting-lodge erected by the tenants of the Bishop of Durham, who apparently was a great hunter. It was built of wood, 60 ft. long and 16 ft. wide, of a simple timber-post construction, with one roof over the whole. Outside, in the shape of lean-to's or small independent wood buildings, were such conveniences as a chamber or garde-le-robe, a steward's room, a kitchen, and a buttery. There was also a chapel for the use of his Lordship. The whole was formed into an enclosure by means of a surrounding palisade.

The Anglo-Saxon farmer lived together with his cattle under a single roof in a barn-like structure, as was the custom in the lands round the Baltic from which he had come. This universal dwelling or barn would be a long, narrow structure, usually made of trunks of trees selected with some kind of a fork on the top so as to give a greater amount of support to the longitudinal timbers which held the roof. The hearth for the fire would probably be at the upper end, and round this the farmer and his household slept. In the centre of the building was often a threshing-floor, and for the convenience of drawing in the corn the entrance to the whole building was usually placed in the wall opposite and made wide enough to admit a loaded wagon. Later on, as the farm grew more prosperous, side-aisles would be constructed with sloping roofs outside the main structure, but communicating directly with it, and to these side-aisles the cattle would be transferred. The side-walls might be constructed of either solid timber or wattle and daub, according to the degree of prosperity of the inhabitants.

The cottages of the humbler countryman or peasant right through the Middle Ages were constructed on the principle of setting up, say, half a dozen natural tree crotches or forks in line, with their open ends resting on the ground or on simple stone foundations, after the style of a chicken's wishbone. Their tops were then joined by a ridge-pole, and further poles as convenient were carried along the sides of the crotches parallel and beneath the ridge-pole on each side. It then became comparatively simple to cover the whole structure in from the ridge-pole to the ground with whatever local material was available. A hole was left for the door, and perhaps another for the window, and there was the dwelling. This, of course, provided only a very simple form of shelter, but soon, using the same principle of construction, it was customary to take bent trees and by putting one saw-cut in them and reversing them, an artificial arch was formed much larger and more substantial than could be obtained from a natural tree crotch. These arches were erected in a line upon stone or brick foundations as required.

It became customary also to divide the roof-space from the

side-walls by placing additional transverse beams, later known as wall-plates, at the appropriate height, thus giving the cottage the outside appearance of the normal roof and wall construction, but in effect none of the weight of the roof was taken by the side-walls, the whole being supported on the roof-arches, which in medieval terms were called " crockes." The roof, as mentioned above, was usually thatched, while the spaces between the upright wall-timbers were filled in with wattle covered with mud or clay, or sometimes in the more superior dwellings a coat of plaster was employed. It was surprising what large dwelling-houses could be erected on this simple form of construction. Such dwellings could, of course, be extended to almost any length, with the human beings accommodated at one end of the structure and the farm animals at the other. Mr Sidney Oldall Addy, M.A., in his extremely interesting book *The Evolution of the English House*, was of the opinion that these " crockes " were always set up at such a distance apart to accommodate a yoke of oxen, these being then the main animals for both ploughing and transport. The space in question was known as a " baie," and was 15 ft. in length.

As mentioned earlier, the dwelling-place of the nobleman or knight was originally one large hall with outbuildings put on indiscriminately for various purposes as convenient. Refinements to this simple state of affairs began to appear about the time of the Norman Conquest. A private room, or solar, for the owner and his family was put on the top end of the hall, reached through a door. Above this might be a simple dormitory for the use of the womenfolk of the household. Gradually this withdrawing-room, as it was called, increased in importance, and the hall became reduced in size. From being the only living-room-cum-dormitory it was used much as a lounge hall is used in a country house to-day. For instance, King Henry III ordered the Sheriff of Nottingham to erect " a great and becoming and fair hall of wood and a kitchen of wood and a withdrawing-room for the Queen's use." In the same enclosure were also a chapel of wood, huts for the domestics, and a mill. This was on the occasion of one of the King's hunting expeditions.

The fifteenth-century timber hall at Rufford measures 47 ft. long by 23 ft. wide, with walls of wood rising to 18 ft. in height. A hammer-beam roof covers the whole, with seven trusses. At the top end is the Baron's seat, some 14 ft. in length and 2 ft. wide. There are doors on each side of this seat leading to the family's withdrawing-room. At the opposite end of the hall is the kitchen space. These medieval halls were lighted by windows placed either on both sides or on one only. Originally they were quite small apertures closed by shutters, and perhaps filled with horn. Later on, however, with the invention of glass, these window-spaces were much enlarged and became an extremely decorative feature. The tendency of baronial halls to be less needed for defence also gave an impetus to the enlargement of the window-space.

The heating of these comparatively large places must always have presented a problem, which, in fact, was never solved. In the early days a fire of wood in the centre of the hall at any rate diffused heat—even if the unfortunate inhabitants were at the same time plagued with smoke ! The only outlet for the smoke was up into the chimney in the roof, where occasionally a simple ventilator was placed to allow it to disperse ultimately. Later stone fireplaces with flues were built in the halls, but these, although overcoming the smoke nuisance, undoubtedly caused most of the heat to go up the chimney. In fact, they could have made little difference to the general temperature of the halls. Finally, the hall became the centre of a number of rooms, either opening out of it or standing round it, and diminished in importance, until at last it became the entrance-hall to a building, consisting of a number of rooms each adapted to its special purpose. The English country house, often known as the Hall, and the pride of our rural landscape, had emerged from its simple Anglo-Saxon prototype.

So far we have dealt with the earl's timbered hall and the peasant's cot, both set in the beautiful English countryside. It is now the turn of the town house, be it the substantial residence of the wealthy alderman or the simple dwelling of the humble shopkeeper. The richly carved half-timbered city house, of which unfortunately so few survive to-day, was a thing of beauty, and reached its zenith in the reign of Queen Elizabeth I. In fact, as will be shown later, there were no substantial improvements in the style of timber building between the days of the early Tudors and the modern scientific methods of timber house construction which were developed in the twentieth century ;

these will be reviewed later in this chapter. The basic principle of design of the town house was the gable. The poorer houses were just one gable, 10 ft. or 12 ft., wide, while the wealthier citizens had houses of a much bigger frontage and constructed of three or four gables. As was pointed out previously, the earliest form of house construction left the roof supported entirely independently of the walls. However, as time went on, especially in the cities, this form of construction was abandoned, and roofs and walls, together with various floors, became a homogeneous unit held together by braces, tenons, and mortices, the whole united with oak pegs. In fact, one house supported another. This led to complicated legislation concerning party walls and precaution against fire. The English Charter called Fitz-Alwyne's Assize, and dated 1189, indicates that the party walls of London houses must be " of free-stone three feet thick and 16 ft. high from which the roof runs up to a point with the gable towards the street." Thatching was forbidden as a roofing material. One of the chief risks to which medieval cities were subjected was that of fire. This is shown by the Ordinances passed by the Common Council following the Great Fire of London. These divided the city into four quarters. For each quarter were to be provided 800 leather buckets, 50 ladders, 24 pick-axes, and 40 shod shovels. In addition each of the twelve principal City Companies was to be responsible to keep in readiness 30 buckets, 1 engine, 6 pick-axes, 3 ladders, and 2 brass hand-squirts. A Bellman was to patrol each Ward from Michaelmas to Lady Day, and diligently to walk up and down the streets from 10 P.M. to 5 A.M. As an additional safeguard, however, a householder upon the cry of fire being raised was to station a competent man at his door well armed and with vessels of water by his side. Also it was laid upon the Companies of Carpenters, Bricklayers, Plasterers, Painters, Smiths, Plumbers, and Paviours to nominate every year from each two master-workmen, four journeymen, eight apprentices, and sixteen labourers to be ready whenever fire broke out to proceed with the Lord Mayor and Sheriffs to quench it. The reason for this imposing array of craftsmen was no doubt that the principal method of preventing the spread of fires in these closely packed streets was to break down or blow up houses so as to produce a fire-break.

THE WOOL HALL, LAVENHAM, SUFFOLK—A FINE EXAMPLE OF HALF-TIMBERED
BUILDING

Photo H. D. Keilor.

As time went on the gables tended to project farther and farther into the already narrow streets, thus reducing them to mere lanes. In fact, in many congested cities it was possible for the citizens to shake hands from the opposite bedroom windows. The building of these projecting gables presented no constructional difficulty, for the heavy beams supporting the first floor were merely allowed to project forward over the wall-plate, 3 ft., 4 ft., or 5 ft., according to the amount of overhang desired. The length of beams enabled the stresses to be distributed over the whole length of the house, and it was therefore possible to carry the gable up for two or even three upper storeys. It was, of course, essential to have strong corner-posts, which were quite frequently shaped out of a whole tree-trunk. In the early city houses, no doubt, wattle and daub were used for filling in between the timber framing, but later on, as more pretentious houses came to be built, rubble and plaster were used, and at the finish of the period brick came into use.

The city house had usually a gable at each end, one looking on to the public street and the other into a narrow garden at the back. As these gables entailed exposure to the weather of the ends of the floor beams and roofing timbers, it was the custom to cover these with barge-boards. It was the elaborate carving of these boards which produced the typical medieval aspect of these narrow streets of timber houses. The barge-boards themselves would be painted and gilded, while the horizontal exposed beam or wall-plate would be carved with the date of the erection of the house, and perhaps the crest or monogram of the householder. The apex of the barge-boards would be formed by a king-post, which in the case of a large house would be carved, and might end in a pinnacle. Originally entrance to the poorer dwellings was literally through a hole in the wall, over which no doubt was hung some piece of rough stuff to keep out the worst of the weather. Soon, however, a door-frame was introduced, and doors were hung. Primitive doors consisted of a number of boards placed edgeways and fastened by two crossed battens. Later fillets were placed over the joints to make them still more weatherproof. Also there came into use on the city streets the heck-door, a door made in two parts of which the lower half could remain shut, while the

A FINE EXAMPLE OF A GABLED FRONT FROM HARVARD HOUSE,
STRATFORD-ON-AVON

Sixteenth century.

upper part could be opened for light and air, and also no doubt
to permit of much neighbourly conversation.

The accounts of a house built in Sheffield in the year 1575
show that the builder was paid the sum of £2 6s. 8d. " for meat
and drink that day the house was reared." This brings us to
the fact that the main constructional timbers of the house were
laid flat on the ground, roughly morticed and tenoned, and
pegged together so as to complete whole sections of the frame-
work. All having been completed, the house was " reared " by
the workmen and friendly neighbours hauling on ropes, and by
the aid of simple tackle. After the house had been given a good
start, so as to say, a feast was provided for the helpers, and the
rest of the day spent in merrymaking. It is said that a timber
house built of wood and plaster is still known in Yorkshire as
a " reared " house, to distinguish it from a brick or stone house.

As indicated earlier, the timber-built house of the rich city
merchant of Elizabethan times was an object of real beauty and
a pleasure to the eye of the beholder. Although every beam,
plank, and board had a constructional purpose, it was the custom
of the time, especially where house-owners of means were concerned, to carve and ornament richly every projecting baulk or
surface, and thus a street of such houses standing cheek by jowl
would produce the effect of being the result of one overall design.
Timber framing also permitted the use of long rows of windows
to give plenty of light, while at the same time avoiding a sense
of heaviness which would have been apparent had large stone
windows been used on small fronts. Window-frames, mullions,
and cills were usually richly carved and moulded. Where the
window was part of a shop, shutters were employed, which
again were ornamented with suitable carvings. So much for the
outside of Elizabethan timbered houses. Inside the walls of the
chief rooms were panelled with simple oak wainscoting. Staircases, which originally had been simple poles with inserted
wooden pegs or rough ladders, became in themselves decorative
features. In due course newel stairs were constructed, and these
led to the fine, wide oak staircases with richly carved rails
and posts which are such a feature of our surviving Tudor
mansions.

While the town houses had been steadily developing from
the original single gable structure to the rich merchant's dwelling,

with its wonderfully ornate and carved frontage, the great noble-man's country hall had grown in luxury in its turn. Many splendid country houses were built by knights and gentlemen towards the end of the Tudor period, and fortunately a number are left to delight us to-day. One of the principal factors which permitted the expansion and adornment of the manor house was, of course, the much greater measure of security that Eliza-bethan days brought to the countryside. The manor houses became a whole complex of rooms, many of them reached by staircases to a second storey. The design of the great hall was also changed, its open roof being often filled with an ornamental plaster ceiling. Many Elizabethan gentlemen were extremely fond of music, and wooden galleries for musicians were fre-quently built at one end of the hall. Talking of the relaxations of the Elizabethan folk brings us to the point that we are fortunate to-day to possess the original contracts for the building of two Shakespearian theatres—namely, the Fortune Theatre, built in 1599, and the Hope Theatre, in 1613. The Fortune contract was made between Philip Henslowe and Edward Alleyn of Southwark on the one part and " Peeter Streete citizen and carpenter of London " on the other.

It is interesting that the main contractor who undertook the erection of the theatre was a carpenter, and embodied in the document is a direction that Peeter Streete is to make all the interior arrangements " as in the late erected Plaie-house on the Banck in the parishe of Ste Saviours called the Globe." Philip Henslowe was also the contracting party in the case of the Hope Theatre, built in 1613. Associated with him on this latter occa-sion was one Jacobe Meade, while again the building contractor was a carpenter Gilbert Katherens of Southwark. He undertook to build not only a theatre, but also a ring for the baiting of bears and bulls. The preamble to the contract is very interesting :

> Before the saide laste daie of November newly erect, builde, and sett vpp one other same place or Plaiehouse fitt & convenient in all thinges, bothe for players to playe in, and for the game of Beares and Bulls to be bayted in the same, and also a fitt and con-venient Tyre house and a stage to be carryed or taken awaie, and to stande vppon tressells good, substanciall, and sufficient for the carryinge and bearinge of suche a stage ; And shall new builde, erect, and sett vp againe the saide plaie house or game place neere

S.C.Wright.

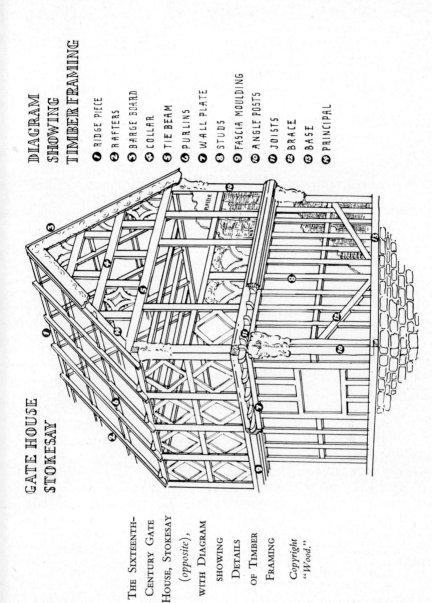

GATE HOUSE
STOKESAY

DIAGRAM
SHOWING
TIMBER FRAMING

❶ RIDGE PIECE
❷ RAFTERS
❸ BARGE BOARD
❹ COLLAR
❺ TIE BEAM
❻ PURLINS
❼ WALL PLATE
❽ STUDS
❾ FASCIA MOULDING
❿ ANGLE POSTS
⓫ JOISTS
⓬ BRACE
⓭ BASE
⓮ PRINCIPAL

The Sixteenth-
Century Gate
House, Stokesay
(*opposite*),
with Diagram
showing
Details
of Timber
Framing

*Copyright
"Wood."*

258 TIMBER : ITS DEVELOPMENT AND DISTRIBUTION

or vppon the saide place, where the saide game place did heretofore stande ; And to builde the same of suche large compasse, fforme, widenes, and height as the Plaie house called the Swan in the libertie of Parris garden in the saide parishe of St Saviour now is.

Note that the carpenter's attention is here drawn to the Swan Theatre, built a few years previously. So we have here mention of no fewer than four theatres built substantially of timber in the London area in less than a score of years—namely, the Globe, the Fortune, the Swan, and the Hope.

It may be said in a certain sense that from the days of Charles II until the commencement of the twentieth century timber almost lost its place as the traditional building material *par excellence* of England. That is not to say that immense numbers of timber buildings of all descriptions, from sheds to barns, and including dwellings of a sort, were not erected, because obviously they were in all parts of the country. But the trend of traditional style had been broken, and wood was merely used as a handy material to run up any kind of structure required to give cover to man or beast. The great houses of the seventeenth and eighteenth centuries were built of either brick or stone. When it came to housing the new industrial population of the nineteenth century brick was the chief constructional material used in the quickly expanding cities and towns. In fact, timber had reverted to being a sort of handmaiden among building materials, instead of holding structural pre-eminence in its own right, as it did down to the end of the seventeenth century.

It was not until the opening of the twentieth century that a few discerning architects rediscovered—if one may be permitted to use this term—the traditional values of wood as a building material in its own right. At first it was employed chiefly in what may well be called owner-occupied houses standing on isolated country sites. Here the value of timber in providing unique residences with a character all their own particularly adapted to our glorious countryside soon made itself felt. One satisfied owner led to another. Such architects as Sir Edwin Lutyens, R.A., with a western red cedar house at Chobham ; Sergius Chermayeff, F.R.I.B.A.—a house in Sussex ; A. M. Chitty, F.R.I.B.A., with a weatherboard constructed house at Churt ; and B. A. LeMare and A. C. Prosham, who designed a guest house for Colonel Sir Stuart Mallinson at Woodford Green, were among the pioneers in this movement to return to wood. A builder who was directly responsible in those days for the construction of a number of admirable timber houses principally using western red cedar and Douglas fir was W. H. Colt. Among others, he built notable residences at Maresfield Park, Pittswater, and Pluckley. It is good to know that Mr

A PAIR OF RURAL HOUSES IN MALAYAN RED MERANTI
By A. L. Osborne, F.R.I.B.A., for Messrs W. H. Colt, Son, and Co.

By courtesy of W. H. Colt, Son, and Co., Bethersden, Kent, Manufacturers.

Colt's pioneer work is being carried on to-day by the firm of Messrs W. H. Colt, Son, and Co.

It was not, however, until nearly twenty years later that in Great Britain any sustained attempt was made to use timber to produce homes in quantity to house the nation's workers and to help solve the housing problem, as such. The way to this particular solution was, of course, pointed by Sweden. Her vast natural forest wealth was an obvious incentive to architects and designers to attempt to solve the problem of providing homes in wood for the country's ever-increasing numbers of industrial workers and their families, more particularly as many of the country's new towns were "Company-towns," built specially for the workers of particular enterprise, and thus lending themselves to controlled design and mass production in its best sense.

It was as early as 1920 that, in Sweden, factory manufacture of prefabricated sections for wood houses started. At first two systems were in vogue. Firstly, one under which the framing and, indeed, the cladding of the building were supplied in pieces all cut to size and length and machined, so that all the builders' men had to do was to assemble them on the site, on the principle of a child's Meccano set ; and, indeed, it was just as simple. The other was a sectional system under which all the wall parts were supplied in large sections so as to be ready to joint up with a minimum of labour on the actual site. The doors and windows were also delivered properly fitted and placed in their frames. This also applied to the interior partitions, floors, and staircases.

It is this Swedish sectional system which interests the United Kingdom most, as naturally this is the form under which practically all the export of Swedish timber houses takes place. Over a score of companies are now believed to be engaged in this trade. The first large contract for Swedish houses for the United Kingdom was placed in 1940, and in March of that year a con-

A PAIR OF SWEDISH SECTIONAL TIMBER HOUSES ERECTED IN THE UNITED
KINGDOM

Copyright "Wood".

signment of these arrived at Bo'ness, to be erected later for Scottish munition workers. Unfortunately the over-running of Norway soon after by the Germans put a stop to this promising venture. However, by the spring of 1944 talk of post-war reconstruction was already in the air, and an exhibition of Swedish prefabricated timber houses was duly opened by Mr Alfred (now Sir Alfred) Bossom. This may be a good moment to define the much abused term 'prefabrication.' The Ministry of Works is on record as defining 'prefabrication' as "the formation of buildings or components for buildings by the assembly of materials or units otherwise than in their final position." And they should know ! To complete our brief survey of Swedish houses, it should be said that large numbers have arrived in this country since the War. Glasgow, for instance, received its first consignment in the autumn of 1945, and the North-west shortly after followed suit. Scotland has readily taken many of the excellent houses. In fact, it can be said that these solidly constructed Swedish wooden houses are peculiarly suited to the rigours of northern climes.

Another type of solid timber construction has been employed by Tarran Industries, Ltd. Here the walls are composed of 3-in. red cedar planks, clad outside with cedar sidings. Inside plaster-boards are nailed to fillets to form an insulation cavity between the plaster-boards and the planks. The 500 houses of this type erected in Dundee have worn well and are extremely popular.

Before proceeding to describe the numerous types of laminated, framed, and hollow timber wall structures, it is only right to refer to the part played by the Timber Development Association, Ltd, in educating the public, both professional and amateur, in the advantages of wood, Great Britain's traditional building material. In June 1938, at Dome Hill, Caterham, the Earl of Crawford and Balcarres opened the first T.D.A. demonstration timber house. This was built in order to show architects, surveyors, and builders how residential districts could be developed with timber homes and have a charm all their own. The carcassing wood of this experimental house consisted of Douglas fir and western hemlock, while the external weather boarding was of painted Baltic redwood. The roof covering was of western red cedar shingles.

In furtherance of its declared aims the Timber Development

Association in 1945 held a Timber House Competition. The writer had the privilege of being one of the assessors, and well remembers the discussions that took place between the ' modernists ' on the one side, and the ' traditionalists ' on the other. At any rate, it was a thoroughly good modern design by John Tingay, A.R.I.B.A., which won the first prize. His house had external walls of vertical cedar boarding, with diagonal boarding nailed to the studding to form the interior lining. The wall units were in prefabricated sections 10 ft. wide, and, as they extended to the eaves, no less than 18 ft. high. The roof was of cedar shingles.

The Seco system deserves special mention, as it was applied to a great number of wartime buildings. Outwardly the Seco structure did not look like a timber building, and, in fact, was constructed of panels 7 ft. by 3 ft., about $1\frac{1}{4}''$ thick, filled with a mixture of woodwool and cement, and faced with sheets of asbestos cement. These panels were supported by hollow plywood beams and by hollow plywood posts as well where necessary. In fact, the use of hollow plywood members was a great feature of the Seco system. In the case of the Seco house the partition walls helped to support the roof. Another feature of the house was stress-skin floors made up of 3-ft. panels running the full length of the room. Four or five of these panels would form the floor, thus doing away with the necessity of separate joists, boards, and ceiling-work.

Another wartime effort was the so-called ' Weybridge ' house, manufactured by the Jicwood Company of that town. The principles of construction of this interesting house were similar to those used in the building of the famous Mosquito wooden aeroplanes. Thin plywood sheets were used to give the walls a sandwich effect, the space between the sheets being filled with wood fibre or expanded rubber to give a total thickness of $1\frac{5}{8}''$ for the external walls. The wall sections extended the full length of the walls, and at the corners were spliced with specially designed splices using waterproof synthetic resin glues. The makers claimed that this system gave better heat-insulation value than the standard 11-in. cavity brick wall. Indeed, the tenants living in one of these houses during the bitterly cold weather of 1947 claimed that they lived far more warmly than in the brick house they had left.

During the War an interesting type of stress-skin plywood construction was first developed by the Forest Products Laboratory at Madison, Wisconsin, U.S.A., for housing munition workers in cases where homes had to be provided rapidly in large quantities. The basic principle was, of course, that the inner and outer skins of plywood assisted in carrying the loads placed upon the walls. Wall-panels were usually 8 ft. high by 4 ft. wide, with a thickness of about 2″. The outer skin consisted of resin-bonded plywood in order to withstand the weather. The skins were glued to small wooden studdings to keep them the proper distances apart.

In 1944–45 the United States sent to this country a number of ' Homosote '-type prefabricated timber houses, but these were found to be of too temporary a nature to meet with much favour as permanent dwellings. An interesting group of new housing innovations was tried out at the end of the War, consisting of structures with brick or steel for the ground floor, and above a top floor made of timber or some other material. A good example of this was the ' Spooner ' house, which was a timber-framed structure using $4\frac{1}{2}″$ brick for the ground-storey walls, and weatherboarding either of British Columbia or Baltic timbers for the upper storey. In 1946 several simple Canadian western red cedar houses were imported into the United

A RILEY-NEWSUM PREFABRICATED TIMBER HOUSE FOR THE EXPORT MARKET
Fox Photos.

Kingdom and erected near Repton. These were typical timber-framed houses, using weatherboards for the outside walls, with roofs of western red cedar shingles.

In 1952 the Riley-Newsum timber house designed and produced in the joinery shops of Messrs H. Newsum Sons and Co., Ltd, Lincoln, was placed on the market in considerable numbers. This house was specially planned for the Canadian market. The accommodation consisted of a living-room with a dining recess ; kitchen and bathroom, with two or three bedrooms at option. Bearing in mind the rigours of the Canadian winter, provision was made for a basement in which the heating installation was kept. Also to guard against the cold, glass-fibre insulation was provided in both the walls and the ceiling ; while the windows were fitted with fly-screens for the hot weather and double storm sashes for the winter. Export orders were received from Canada and Australia, the houses being sent abroad in groups of eight. Each consignment consisted of 104 crates and 64 bundles of pre-cut timber pieces, the whole weighing 96 tons.

In conclusion, it is surely an interesting and stimulating fact that in this twentieth-century age of metals, new alloys, and scientific research, wood has returned to the field as a serious factor in primary housing construction, quite apart from joinery and interior trim. In fact, an entirely new branch of science in the shape of wood technology has been born, and will undoubtedly exercise great influence on future developments. It is good to see this new kind of industrial research reanimating an old and tried material like timber. There is always the danger of established commodities resting on their ancient merits. This temptation is obviously being resisted in the timber industry to-day. There is no doubt that the future will see still further developments in timber houses, employing wood maybe in a number of forms far removed from the original Elizabethan traditional treatment.

CHAPTER XV

WOODEN SHIPS

IN our opening chapter it was said that the Egyptians were the first people to depict on the walls of their tombs ancient carpenters and joiners at work. Now, in our concluding chapter, we can give the Egyptians further credit for their pictures of early ships. Several Egyptian temples of the New Kingdom period have engraved on their walls scenes of conquests and trade which include ships. Among the most noteworthy are the Temples of Pharaoh Thothmes and Queen Hatshephut. These Egyptian sea-going ships had a high bow and stern with a low waist. They were fitted with one mast and a single large lateen sail very much like the Arab dhows which sail the Red Sea to-day. No doubt they were built of cedar and fir brought from Lebanon, as there was no timber in Egypt. These ships were accustomed to make long ocean-going voyages, for instance, to Tarshish, which was on the south coast of Spain, and to the land of Punt, which was probably situate in East Africa.

The Phœnicians, Greeks, and Romans in their turn were all great builders of wooden ships. Some were provided with sails, and others, as in the case of the Roman triremes, with three banks of oarsmen. All three nations could in case of need put on the seas large seaworthy fleets. From what ancient authors tell us their building did not take long. Here is a quotation from Evelyn's *Sylva* on this point :

If you are to remove your timber, let the dew be first off, and the south wind blow before you draw it ; neither should you by any means put it to use for three or four months after, (some not till as many years) unless great necessity urge you, as it did Duillius, who, in the first Punic War, built his fleet of timber before it was seasoned, being not above two months from the very felling to the launching ; the navy of Hiero was forty five days from the forest to the sea, and that of Scipio, in the second Carthaginian War, only forty.

The Norwegian Viking Olaf Tryggvesson, who flourished in Norway round about the year A.D. 1000, is recorded as having possessed a ship, *The Long Serpent*, which was no less than 120 ft. in length and capable of carrying 600 men. The vessels of this time were at any rate partially decked. In the stern was a cabin where the commander had his quarters, while in the prow was another covered space in which the King's standard-bearers and their insignia were accommodated. A long ridge-pole was provided to set up over the deck, and at night this could be covered with a canvas or cloth, so that the fighting men might have some protection from the weather as they slept. These Viking ships were usually built of oak timbers. The Sagas contain numerous references to the " oaken Ships."

The Saxon King Harold was one of the most notable sea-captains of his time, and had a great love for the sea. We are fortunate in possessing a picture of his ship, *The Black Swan*, depicted in the Bayeux Tapestry. From contemporary information contained in the Anglo-Saxon Chronicle and other sources it would appear that the ship might well have been over 50 ft. long. These early Saxon boats were clinker-built—that is to say, the boards overlapped one another, giving additional strength and enabling the vessels to be roughly caulked to keep down leakage. They were steered by a sort of paddle, and it was customary to paint the sides of the ships in long horizontal stripes, yellow, red, and blue being popular colours.

King Edward III was a great warrior and fought many campaigns in France, for which he needed many ships. From the chronicles of Froissart and other contemporary writers of the fourteenth century it can be seen that already many specialized forms of vessels sailed the seas. The carrack, a pattern originating in the Mediterranean, was one of the largest ships. These were broad in proportion to their length, sometimes as much as the ratio of 1 to 3. Indeed, they had to be so constructed in order to carry unwieldy castles on both bow and stern. These would have made an ordinary boat quite top-heavy. They were sea-worthy as a class only because the hulls narrowed very much above the water-line—" tumblehome sides," as the English Navy called them. It is said that two carracks from Spain were 1000 and 1300 tons respectively.

The carracks were fitted with a considerable number of cabins,

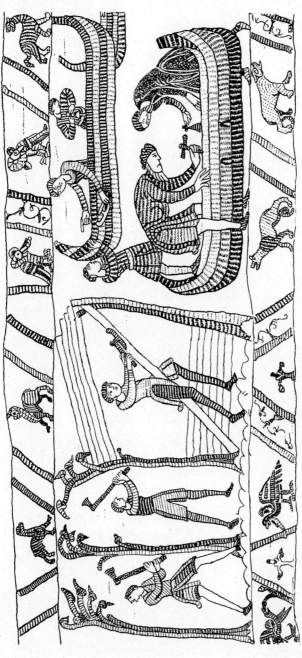

NORMAN CRAFTSMEN (on the left) FELLING TREES AND TRIMMING PLANKS FOR THE CLINKER-BUILT BOATS IN PROCESS OF
COMPLETION (on the right)

From the Bayeux Tapestry.

including such domestic conveniences as pantries, butteries, and
larders.   In many cases these great ships were splendidly painted
in red, blue, and other bright colours.   Great use was made of
gilt inlay on the poops, and in the case of royal ships it was
customary to paint the King's Arms on shields at various points
round the bulwarks.   A number of banks of oars manned by
several rowers to each were needed to drive them.   Galliots or
galleys were built for speed, and relied upon both sails and oars.
They were long, narrow, three-masted vessels and carried on a
crossyard triangular lateen sails.   They were accustomed to fight
in line with their bows towards the enemy.   A strong bulwark
was built across the foredeck to protect the rowers from plunging
fire.   Galleasses were another form of galley, with larger square
sails and rounded bows.   Cogs, or small merchantmen, were
broad in proportion to their length, in order to accommodate
the greatest possible quantity of goods.   They must have been
difficult to sail except with a following or cross wind.   Liques,
lynes, pessons, and doggers were all used for fishing on various
parts of the coast, pickards, a light form of pinnace, being largely
used in harbours and sheltered waters.

One John Alastre, a royal clerk at Bayonne, in Southern
France, writes to King Henry V in the year 1419 to tell his royal
master about a ship that was building for the King in the local
dockyard.   The keel had been laid down and was 112 ft. long,
while the hull had already been built to a height of 36 strakes.
Across the top of the strakes fifteen beams had been laid to carry
the deck.   The longest beam was 46 ft., so this would have been
the approximate breadth of the vessel.   The worthy clerk further
complains that the royal carpenters were negligent and did not
trouble to go into the countryside to obtain the best possible
timber.

The old Pipe Rolls give the expenses involved in laying down
the galliot *La Phelipe* at Lynn in the year 1336.   She had one
mast only, which cost £10 ; a yard at £3 and a bowsprit at
£2 3s. 4d.   The yard supported a sail which was dyed red, with
an area of 640 ells.   In addition to the sail, provision was made
for 80 oars for use in calm weather.   One large anchor of Spanish
iron and five small anchors were provided.   The larger fighting
ships, such as carracks and galleons, carried wooden castles at
both fore and stern.   These were put on after the construction

of the vessels by a special class of carpenters known as castle-wrights. Should the King find it necessary to call up large merchantmen for his service in time of war, then it was customary to add these fighting castles to their superstructures before they joined the Royal Fleet. For example, in 1336 the *Trinity*, a merchantman of 200 tons, was given an aftcastle and a topcastle.

Henry VII may truly be called the parent of the British Royal Navy, because it was in his later days that the great ship *Henry Grâce à Dieu*, otherwise known as the *Great Harry*, was commenced, although it was not completed until the reign of his successor, Henry VIII. The successful launching of this ship caused a considerable stir in naval circles of the period, and there are consequently many references to her in current chronicles. She is said to have cost the King nearly £14,000. She was built by one William Bond, said to have been the first master ship-wright of the Royal Navy, under the direction of the Royal Clerk of the Ships, named Brygandine. She was well equipped for sail, having four masts with a bowsprit set at an acute angle. The sail area carried by the mast was broken up by the use of three yardarms. Each principal mast bore two fighting-tops in which were posted small-arms men to annoy the enemy.

The *Henry Grâce à Dieu* was one of the first vessels to be furnished with portholes for the use of cannon of the largest size—*i.e.*, culverins, carrying an 18-lb. ball, and demi-culverins, with a 9-lb. ball. In addition a number of small pieces of ord-nance such as sakers (5-pounders), minnions (4-pounders), and falcons (2-pounders) were mounted on the fore and aft castles. This ship was still part of the Royal Fleet in the reign of Edward VI, as will be seen from the following extract from a contem-porary Muster Roll :

5 Jan. Anno R.R. Ed. VI. primo
Shippes at Wolwidge.
The *Henry Grâce à Dieu*, 1000-tons, Souldiers 349, Marryners 301, Gonners 50, Brass Pieces 19, Iron Pieces 103.

In spite, however, of this favourable record, it would be a mistake to think that these wooden ships were necessarily long-lived. The records show that durability was not the virtue of Tudor ship construction, the principal reason being that many of them were built of unseasoned wood.

The building of a large ship having been determined, the Royal Officers would then proceed to search the country for suitable oak. In a few cases seasoned plank may have been available, but more commonly the trees were felled and converted into dimension stock then and there. It is clear that many ships, particularly those constructed under pressure in time of war, commenced to rot almost from the day they entered the water. In fact, the Royal Fleet fell into such neglect during the uncertain time following the reign of Henry VIII that by the time Queen Elizabeth came to the throne an effective fleet was no longer in being. At the outset of the reign the great Naval Commander Hawkins of Plymouth was called upon to draw up a report on the state of the royal ships. The following is a quotation :

> In the purchase and disposal of timber and plank, great abuses prevail. Since 1570 the Queen has paid £9,000 for these materials, and not £4,000 worth has been used in her service. The purveyors of timber, using the royal prerogative of compulsory purchase at fixed prices, make great profits, for they sell the best of the material for private use and make the state pay extremely for the refuse. When the quality is considered, the Queen does not get one-third of the value she pays for. The master-shipwrights corroborate these statements.

Under the stimulus, however, of a covert or cold war with Spain, the Queen's Navy was quickly reconstituted, but even then the following list of the English Fleet in the year 1588, the year of the Armada, drawn from the Cotton MS., shows that in that time of great emergency the Royal Fleet had to draw to itself a mixed levy of ships from all quarters :

A List of the English Fleet in the Year 1588

Men of War belonging to Her Majesty....................... 17
Other Ships hired by Her Majesty for this service............ 12
Furnished by the City of London, being double the number the
    Queen demanded, all well manned, and thoroughly provided
    with ammunition and provision 16
Tenders and Store-ships.................................... 4
Furnished by the City of Bristol large and strong ships, and
    which did excellent service.............................. 3
A Tender... 1
From Barnstaple, merchant Ships converted into Frigates...... 3

From Exeter 2
A Stout Pinnace 1
From Plymouth stout ships, every way equal to the Queen's
Men of War 7
A Fly-Boat 1
Under the Command of Lord Henry Seymour in the narrow
seas, of the Queen's ships and Vessels in her service......... 16
Ships fitted out at the expense of the Nobility Gentry and
Commons of England.................................. 43
By the Merchant-adventurers prime Ships and excellently well
furnished 10
Sir William Winter's pinnace............................. 1
                                                        ——
                                                        137
                                                        ——

The flagship in which Lord Howard of Effingham hoisted
his flag to sail against the Armada was the *Ark Royal*. Sir Walter
Raleigh had this fine vessel constructed in 1587, and then sold
her to Queen Elizabeth for the sum of £5000. She was built
on galleon lines, with high bulwarks and fighting castles at bow
and stern. These castles were used to repel boarders, and mounted
small guns for this purpose. In addition they furnished living
quarters for the crew. The *Ark Royal* had several masts and
carried a big spread of canvas. Her displacement was 800 tons,
and she carried a crew of about 1000 men. The following is
an extract from an Elizabethan book on navigation, the chapter
being entitled " The Manner of Building " :

The next consideration is the manner of building, which in
shipps of warr is of greatest importance because therein consists
both their sayling and force. The shipps that can saile best can
take or leave, (as they say) and use all advantages the winds and
seas does afford ; and their mould, in the judgement of men of
best skill, both dead and alive, should have the length treble to the
breadth, but not to draw above 16 foote water, because deeper
shipps are seldom goode saylers, and ever unsafe for our rivers,
and for the shallow harbours, and all coasts of ours, or other seas.
Besides, they must bee somewhat snugg built, without double
gallarys, and too lofty upper workes, which overcharge many
shipps, and make them looke faire, but not to worke well at sea.

In comparison with the English Fleet, the Spanish Armada
consisted of 65 galleons, or great ships ; 25 urcas, or cargo boats

from 300 to 700 tons ; 19 dispatch vessels from 70 to 100 tons ;
13 zabras ; 4 galleasses, or large galleys, and 4 smaller ; in all,
130 vessels with a complement of about 30,000 seamen and
soldiers.   Contemporary opinion was that although the larger
Spanish ships were a little bigger than the largest English, the
ships of the Royal Navy at any rate had a decided superiority
of armament, and in addition were far more handy in a seaway.
The extremely lofty forecastles and poops of the Spaniards made
them very difficult to manœuvre in a wind, and at the same time
presented magnificent targets to the English cannon.   Nevertheless the great ships of the Armada must have been a splendid
sight.   At both bow and stern their superstructures were bright
with gilt and colour.   Many famous artists were employed on
the most elaborate carvings.   The sails were both painted and
embroidered in many gay colours.   In some cases the design was
a large red cross, or, again, the crest of some great nobleman
or the armorial bearings of a famous port.   Streamers thirty
yards long fluttered from their mastheads, and flying proudly
were the flags of Philip II and of the various commanders.

James I, as can well be imagined, was no great sailor, and the
Prince Royal was the only notable ship launched during his reign.
Her chief constructor was one Phineas Pett, Master of Arts of
Emmanuel College, Cambridge, first of the great Pett family
of shipbuilders.   The ship at the time was considered to be of
great beauty, and the following quotation from the historian
Stowe shows the feeling of the time concerning her :

> This year the King builded a most goodly ship for warre, the
> keel whereof was 114 feet in length, and the cross beam was 44
> feet in length ; she will carry 64 pieces of ordnance, and is of the
> burthen of 1,400 tons.   This royal ship is double built, and is most
> sumptuously adorned, within and without, and all manner of curious
> carving, painting and rich gilding, being in all respects the greatest
> and goodliest ship that ever was builded in England ; and this
> glorious ship the King gave to his son, Henry, the prince of Wales ;
> and the 24th of September, the king, the queen, the prince of
> Wales, and the duke of York and lady Elizabeth, with many great
> lords, went unto Wolwidge to see it launched.

In spite of the eulogies lavished on the *Prince Royal* at the
time of her launching, she was, although a striking picture, both
badly designed and built.   In the year 1621 Buckingham was

The "Ark Royal," Flagship of Queen Elizabeth I's Navy

British Museum.

LORD HOWARD OF EFFINGHAM, LORD HIGH ADMIRAL OF THE NAVAL FORCES
WHICH DEFEATED THE ARMADA

informed that although the ship had cost £20,000, a further £6000 would have to be spent to make her fit for service, she having been constructed of green, unseasoned timber.

The "Royal Sovereign," a 100-gun Ship built in 1637

From a contemporary picture.

Charles I was more conscientious and loved the sea. It was in 1637 that the *Sovereign of the Seas*, later named the *Royal Sovereign*, was designed by Phineas Pett and built under the supervision of another member of that family named Peter. We cannot do better than quote from the contemporary description of the ship by Thomas Heywood :

> Her length by the keele is 128 foote, or thereabout, within some few inches. Her mayne breadth or widenesse from side to side 48 foote. Her utmost length from the fore-end of the sterne, a prora ad puppim, 232 foote. She is in height, from the bottome of her keele to the top of her lanthorne, 76 foote. She hath three flush deckes and a forecastle, an halfe decke, a quarter decke, and a round house. Her lower tyre hath thirty ports, which are to be furnished with demi-cannon and whole cannon throughout, being able to beare them. Her middle tyre hath also thirty ports for demi-culverin and whole culverin. Her third tyre hath twenty-sixe ports for other ordnance. Her forecastle hath twelve ports, and her halfe decke hath fourteene ports. She carrieth eleaven anchors, one of them weighing foure thousand foure hundred, etc. and according to these are her cables, mastes, sayles, cordage.

At this time there was a universal tendency to over-gun ships, and in consequence at sea many were dismounted and stowed in the hold as ballast. The price of guns varied from £12 to £15 per ton, and the King's gunfounders had virtually a monopoly. The range for all guns was Ratcliffe Fields, and their export without licence was forbidden.

The Commonwealth period was a time of almost continuous war with the Dutch, and naval expenditure was, comparatively speaking, enormous. In the year 1656 a sum of £809,000 was voted to the Navy out of a total revenue of £1,050,000 ; in 1657, £624,000 out of £951,000 ; and in 1658, £848,000 out of £1,517,000. There were Government dry docks at Chatham, Woolwich, Deptford, and Blackwall, but as these were not sufficient many ships were built and launched at private yards at Blackwall, Ratcliffe, Limehouse, Wapping, Woodbridge, Yarmouth, etc. This was the first time that ships began to be qualified by formal ratings, for example, first rates—80 guns and upward ; second rates—52 and upward ; third rates—44 and upward ; fourth rates—32 and upward ; and fifth rates—12 and upward. In other words, naval architecture as related to fighting

A Dutch Second-rater of about 1670, the Time of the Naval Wars of King Charles II's Reign

From a contemporary picture.

ships began to take the form which reached its height in Nelson's famous fleet at the battle of Trafalgar. Charles II carried on the Commonwealth legacy of naval wars with the Dutch, and in consequence this was a period of considerable shipbuilding activity.

Fortunately for us Phineas Pett kept a copious journal, and from it we have the details of a journey he made with Sir Anthony Deane into the counties of Suffolk and Norfolk for the purpose of buying timber for His Majesty's service for the completing of no fewer than thirty ships authorized by Act of Parliament in the year 1677. Our friend obtained a promise from Sir Charles Gaudys that he would sell to the King the following spring 300 or 350 of his best oak-trees at the then market price, the question of quality being taken into consideration. They also made purchases of timber for prompt delivery, as will be seen from the following quotation :

> We bought all his plank at 5L. per load, as the board directed, when he was at London. We bought 50 load of compass timber for foothooks, such as the master shipwright shall choose, at 45s. per load on the place. He would have sold the timber at 40s. per load but we buried his demand on the plank in the timber, as agreed at the board. From Crow's Hall we went to Otley, where we found the carters carrying away a sternpost for the new ship at Harwich, and the rest converting on the ground as fast as could be. From thence we departed, and lay at Ipswich that night.

The phraseology is curious, but apparently they paid the worthy knight more than he asked for his compass timber in order to make certain of securing the seasoned plank, which no doubt was in short supply. By the way, the term " compass " timber probably means hewn balks. The following week our negotiators bought from Mr John Lee at Laxfield 100 loads of 4″ oak plank and 100 loads of 3″ ditto at £4 15s. per load delivered Harwich ; also 60 loads of large compass timber very good and well grown, to be delivered to Woodbridge at the rate of 55s. per load. The journal tells us that they spent the rest of the day in filling up warrants for the Justice of the Peace to impress both men and wagons for the carriage of the timber ; also in writing letters telling of their doings to the Admiralty Board in London.

Mr Samuel Pepys, the renowned diarist, was Secretary to the Board of Admiralty in the reign of Charles II, and must consequently have had many dealings with the chief constructor, Phineas Pett. In his diary Pepys has much to tell us of the difficulties of keeping a fleet in being to face the belligerent Dutch, it being hard to get money from the Treasury against the competing claims of the royal mistresses. His critics alleged that the dilapidated state of the ships was due to the great quantity of foreign timber used in their construction. Seeing, however, that the King's fleet had been lying dismantled and uncared for in the river Medway for no less than five years, the condition of the vessels was not surprising ! The Secretary for the Navy, however, begged his detractors to show him where enough English Oak plank of sufficient dimensions for the building of the great ships could be got. In fact, he conducted a long correspondence with the shipwright to prove that sufficient English timber was unobtainable. Finally he demanded and obtained a Parliamentary Commission of Inquiry. This body, after hearing the evidence from the leading Thames shipbuilders, decided that for vessels of over 300 tons burden Prussian and Bohemian timbers were cheaper, more reliable, and more enduring than English wood. Our friend was nothing if not thorough in his actions !

Turning from timber to an even more universal subject, we cannot refrain from giving an extract from the diary of a Naval Chaplain, Henry Teonge, who was at sea from 1675 to 1679 :

> Off Lisbon our noble Capt. feasted the officers of his small squadron with 4 dishes of meate, viz. 4 excellent henns and a piece of pork boyled, in a dish ; a giggett of excellent mutton and turnips ; a piece of beife or 8 ribbs, well seasoned and roasted ; and a couple of very fatt greene geese ; last of all a greate chesshyre cheese ; for drink we had Canary, Sherry, Renish, Clarett, white wine, syder, beare, ale and punch.

It is an interesting comparison that in the year 1706 the cost of the hull, masts, and yards of a first-rate ship of the line mounting 100 guns was £31,994, with rigging and stores of £6587, making a grand total of £38,581 ; while in the same year the cost of a small 20-gun sloop was for the hull, masts, and yards £2176, with rigging and stores £962, giving a total of £3138.

A little more than 150 years earlier Admiral Hawkins in the report which he made to Queen Elizabeth recorded that in the year 1545 a 450-ton ship " honestly built " cost £4 per ton, or, say, £1800 for the Elizabethan vessel. It is interesting to recall that it was in some such ship as this that Christopher Columbus crossed the Atlantic and discovered America.

An outstanding ship built for the Royal Navy in the early days of the eighteenth century was the *Royal George*. She mounted an armament exceeding that of any vessel possessed by the French or Spaniards. Her full specification, taken from a contemporary document which speaks for itself, is as follows :

" Royal George," built at Woolwich ; taken in hand the 8th of January, 1746 ; launched the 1st of February, 1756.

Dimensions	Feet	Inches
Length of the keel, for tonnage	143	$5\frac{1}{2}$
Length of the gun-deck	178	0
Extreme breadth	51	$9\frac{1}{2}$
Depth in the hold	21	6
Burthen in tons 2046		
Guns 90		

Timber expended in building

	Loads	Feet
Strait oak timber	2309	6
Compass oak timber	2306	40
Elm ditto	125	10
Fir ditto	214	8
Knees, square,	170	8
Ditto, raking	149	33
English oak plank, 4 inches thick	135	8
Ditto, 3 ditto	94	9
Ditto, $2\frac{1}{2}$ ditto	17	33
Ditto, 2 ditto	15	4
Dantzick ditto 4 ditto	174	4
Ditto, 3 ditto	42	13
Elm ditto 4 ditto	4	39
Ditto 3 ditto	2	0

N.B.   50 cubic feet of timber make one load.

It will be seen, therefore, that a little under 5760 loads or 288,000 ft. cube of timber were required to build one " First Rater."

No wonder the state of England's woodlands was a continual preoccupation with Government during the prolonged naval wars of the seventeenth and eighteenth centuries.

During the Seven Years War (1756–63) a class of vessel was introduced which was of the greatest value to the Navy. This was a highly developed frigate, carrying a heavy armament on one deck and built with clean lines to cruise at a good all-round speed. Two notable frigates were the *Palace* and the *Brilliant*, constructed under the superintendence of Sir Thomas Slade in 1757. The principal enemies of the English shipping were the French frigates, and, in order to counteract their qualities of swift sailing, an experiment was even made of building frigates of fir instead of oak, so as to lighten their displacement. The need for fast sailing-ships about this time also produced a number of experiments in coppering ships' bottoms to preserve them against worm and fouling.

So far we have been talking of ships mainly built of oak timbers, but it is opportune to speak at this point of another great shipbuilding timber—teak. This wood has been used for boat-building in the East from time immemorial. It is an Indian tradition that Alexander the Great employed many Indian shipwrights to build ships of teak for the fleet that accompanied his army on their return march from the mouth of the river Indus to Persia. The famous Venetian explorer of the thirteenth century, Marco Polo, also described in his diary Indian ships that were so large as to be able to carry 6000 bags of pepper and required a crew of no fewer than 300 men to work them. However, teak was first brought to the notice of English shipbuilders and the Admiralty through the medium of the East India Company and their Bombay dockyard. It was, in fact, in the year 1668 that the Court of Directors first wrote to their Administrative Board in Bombay saying that they considered it would be advantageous for the Company's trade if a dockyard and shipbuilding establishment were built at the port of Bombay. The Directors' wishes were obeyed, and during the last decade of the seventeenth century a number of small vessels suitable for local navigation were built in this yard, but it was not until 1736 that the first warship the *Drake*, a schooner of 14 guns, was built for the East India Company's own Navy. Other similar vessels were completed in quick succession to sail under the Honourable Company's flag. Then in the year 1805 the *Pitt*, a frigate of 36 guns, was built in teak for George III's Navy. Another frigate, the *Salsette*, was built for the British Navy in 1807. This ship aroused more contemporary comment than the *Pitt*, as it was brought to England and extensive tests on its construction and sailing qualities were carried out in the royal dockyards. Other ships for the British Navy followed, the climax being reached in two second-rate ships of the line, the *Ganges* and the *Calcutta*, both being built in 1821, each mounting 84 guns. All these vessels, whether large or small, were built of teak, and we find continual minutes in the proceedings of the Court of Directors and other bodies on the great advantages of this timber for shipbuilding. For instance, in 1734 the Bombay Public Department issued a memorandum on the great advantage of teak for shipbuilding above all other Eastern woods, and urged upon the Court of Directors the necessity for obtaining adequate supplies of the wood for their dockyard. It appears that the Indian shipwrights, besides building in a very durable wood—namely, teak—made a practice of rabbiting the sheathing-plank of their ships and then caulking the outside with cotton and pitch in such an excellent way that the ships' bottoms were practically watertight, and consequently the hulls required very little pumping to keep them dry.

The history of the Bombay Dockyard is virtually wrapped up with the story of the famous Wadia family of master-shipbuilders. Lowjee, the first of that ilk, came to Bombay in 1736, and was immediately appointed Master Carpenter at the dockyard by the Council, a post which he filled with great honour and distinction for nearly forty years. Following Lowjee, no fewer than nine members of the Wadia family held without a break in the succession the post of Master Carpenter and builder of the Bombay Dockyard. In fact, it was upon the retirement of Jamsetjee Wadia that the post was finally abolished in 1885, thus making a total period of 150 years during which this famous family of Indian shipbuilders had maintained their contact with the Bombay Dockyard.

The Napoleonic Wars, the necessity of blockading the coast of France and Spain, and other naval operations produced extreme activity in shipbuilding in all the yards of the country, both

Government and private. The table shown below indicates the enormous output of battleships of all descriptions :

Cruising Ships, exclusive of Harbour and Stationary Vessels, Troop and Storeships, Ships building, etc., at the Beginning of each Year										
Class	1793	1794	1795	1796	1797	1798	1799	1800	1801	1802
First-rates . . .	5	6	6	6	6	6	6	6	6	6
Second-rates . .	16	16	17	16	16	17	17	16	16	16
Third-rates . .	92	95	91	94	94	97	102	101	105	104
Total of the line .	113	117	114	116	116	120	125	123	127	126
Fourth-rates . .	12	12	12	21	16	16	14	14	13	13
Fifth-rates . . .	79	84	102	106	115	123	117	112	113	120
Sixth-rates . .	35	36	35	37	40	41	42	34	34	28
Sloops . . .	40	53	62	84	91	94	98	107	104	98
Bombs . . .	2	2	2	2	2	11	15	15	14	14
Fireships . . .	5	3	3	3	3	3	7	7	3	2
Brigs, cutters, etc. .	18	21	33	36	52	94	99	97	103	104
Grand Total . .	304	328	363	405	435	502	517	509	511	505

The total tonnage of the vessels enumerated above was, in 1793, 295,409, and in 1802 416,566.

Concerning the shipbuilding of the period 1793 to 1802, there is little that needs saying. Naval architecture underwent but small changes. In 1794 the Admiralty directed that frigates, from the 32's upward, should in future be constructed with four-inch instead of three-inch bottoms. About the same time it was decided to give ships of war greater length in proportion to their beam than had been customary in Great Britain, and to raise the lower batteries in new vessels of the higher rates. Fir, as a material for hulls, was reintroduced for sloops in 1796, after it had been disused since 1757 ; and in 1797 seven frigates with hulls of the same wood were under construction. All this active shipbuilding did not produce much alteration in design or practice. No doubt, in order to economize on oak and also to reduce their displacement, a number of frigates and the lesser ships were built of fir timbers. Also the practice was introduced of using diagonal instead of square or rectangular timbers, so as to gain

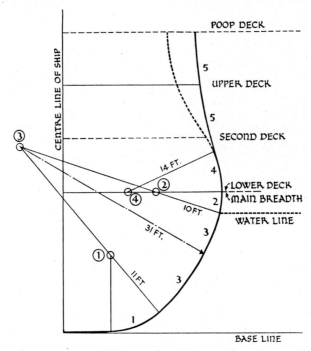

A DIAGRAM FROM "HISTORY OF MARINE ARCHITECTURE,"
(1802), BY JOHN CHARNOCK, F.S.A.

additional strength. The fleet which fought under Nelson at
Trafalgar may be said to have represented the zenith of the
wooden ships of war. As far as the utilization of timber was
concerned, the designers could do no more.

The backbone of the British fleet, however, the great first-,
second-, and third-raters which constituted the class known as
' ships of the line,' were probably the most efficient wooden
battleships ever to sail the seas. It is opportune, therefore, at
this juncture to give the dimensions of Nelson's first-rater, the
Victory. The length of the gun-deck was 186 ft., keel 151 ft.,
depth 21 ft. 6 in. Her displacement was 2162 tons, mounting
100 guns, with a crew of 150 men. The *Victory* was built at
Chatham in 1765, the surveyor-in-charge being the famous Sir
Thomas Slade, and the master-builder, Mr E. Allen.

Up to the end of the eighteenth century the Royal Navy
ships were customarily painted with bright yellow sides and blue

upperworks, the interiors being generally coated red. Nelson,
for a number of reasons, caused his ships to be painted black,
with yellow strakes along each line of gun-ports. This method
of painting was known as chequer painting, and, as will be seen
from the numerous coloured prints of the period, distinguished
practically all the British ships which took part in the battle of
Trafalgar. Against this the enemy favoured painting their ships
a variety of colours from all black to yellow with a red streak.
The famous Spanish flagship the *Santissima Trinidad* had four lines
of red with a white ribbon between each. The *Victory*, still
afloat at Portsmouth, is a typical ship of her day.

BIBLIOGRAPHY

Chapters I–V

Pepys's *Diary*.

Evelyn's *Sylva*.

Select Committee of the House of Commons on Timber Duties, 1835.

PERRY, THOMAS D. : *Modern Plywood* (Pitman, 1947).

CAMPBELL, R. : *The London Tradesman* (third edition, London, 1757).

JENNINGS, L. G. : "A Glossary of Log and Timber Measures," in the *Timber Trades Journal*, 1956.

WILSON, S. E. : "The Hoppus System" (1955–56), in the *Timber Trades Journal*, etc., in various articles.

SALZMANN, L. F. : *English Trade in the Middle Ages* (Clarendon Press, Oxford, 1931).

REDDAWAY, T. F. : *The Rebuilding of London after the Great Fire* (Cape, 1940).

CLIFFORD, FREDERICK : *A History of Private Bill Legislation* (two vols., London, 1885–87).

HOPE, W. H. ST JOHN : *Windsor Castle* (Country Life, 1913).

Chapter VI

SODERLUND, E. F. : *Swedish Timber Exports, 1850–1950* (Swedish Wood Exporters' Association).

A Reply to the Observations of a British Merchant on the Select Committee of the House of Lords relative to the Timber Trade (1821).

BROWN, J. C. : *Forest and Forestry of Northern Russia and Lands Beyond* (Edinburgh, 1884).

— : *Forestry in Norway* (Edinburgh, 1884).

— : *Finland : its Forests and Forest Management* (Edinburgh, 1883).

— : *Forests and Forestry in Poland* (Edinburgh, 1885).

MALLET, P. H. : *De la Ligue Hanséatique* (Geneva, 1805).

Chapter VII

TYSON, WARREN S. : *A Mirror for Americans* (Chicago University Press).

WILSON, LILLIAN M. : *Forest Conservation in Colonial Times* (The Forest Products History Foundation, Minnesota, 1948).

HORN, STANLEY F., *Southern Lumberman* (Nashville, Tennessee, U.S.A.)
— : *This Fascinating Lumber Business* (Bobbs, Merrill, New York, 1943).

Chapter VIII

Select Committee of the House of Commons on Timber Duties, 1835.
British Columbia Lumber and Shingle Manufacturers' Association publications.
DE LA ROCHE, MAZO : *Quebec : Historic Seaport* (Macmillan, 1946).
GILLIES, DAVID, and WHITTON, CHARLOTTE : *A Hundred Years A-Fellin'* (privately published Ontario, 1942).
HARVEY, A. G. : *Douglas of the Fir* (a biography of David Douglas) (Harvard University Press, 1947).

Chapter IX

Diaries of Celia Fiennes, 1692–95.
ST PIERRE, BERNARDIN DE : *Studies of Nature* (3 vols., London, 1798).
OGILBY, JOHN : *America* (London, 1671).
SHERATON, THOMAS : *Cabinet Dictionary* (London, 1805).
CHALONER AND FLEMING : *The Mahogany Tree in the West Indies* (Liverpool, 1851).
"J. E. H." : *The Mahogany and Foreign Timber Trade of Liverpool* (Manchester, 1883).
BLOME, RICHARD : *A Description of the Island of Jamaica* (London, 1672).
SYMONS, R. W. : "Early Imports of Mahogany for Furniture," in *Connoisseur*, 1934.

Chapter X

Reports on Teak Forests, 1837–50 (India Office Files).
FALCONER, H. : *Report on the Teak Forests of the Tenasserim Provinces* (Calcutta, 1852).
BRANDIS, D. : *Report on the Teak Forests of Pegu, 1856* (London, 1860).
Files of the Bombay Burmah Trading Corporation, Ltd.

Chapter XI

Evelyn's *Sylva*.
COOK, MOSES : *The Manner of Raising, Ordering and Improving Forest Trees* (third edition, London, 1724).

RODGERS, JOHN :   *The English Woodland* (Batsford, 1941).
BROWN, J. C. :   *The Forests of England* (Edinburgh, 1883).

Chapter XII

Proceedings of the Newcomen Society.
Proceedings of the Royal Society.
RICHARDS, J. :   *A Treatise on the Construction and Operation of Wood-working Machines* (London, 1872).

Chapter XIII

JUPP, E. B., and POCOCK, W. W. :   *An Historical Account of the Worshipful Company of Carpenters of the City of London* (London, 1887).
ANDREWS, FRANCIS B. :   *The Mediæval Builder and his Methods* (Oxford University Press, 1925).
HARVEY, JOHN :   *English Mediæval Architects* (Batsford, 1954).
ELTRINGHAM, G. J. :   *The Timber Wharf of the Carpenters Company of London* (privately published).

Chapter XIV

LLOYD, NATHANIEL :   *A History of the English House* (Architectural Press, 1949).
BELL, W. G. :   *The Great Fire of London in 1666* (Lane, 1920).
ADDY, SIDNEY O. :   *The Evolution of the English House* (Allen and Unwin, 1933).
SAUNDERS, HILARY ST GEORGE :   *Westminster Hall* (Michael Joseph, 1951).
CROSSLEY, FREDERICK H. :   *Timber Building in England* (Batsford, 1951).
Timber Development Association brochure on Timber Houses.
HODGES, C. WALTER :   *The Globe Restored* (Benn, 1953).

Chapter XV

WADIA, R. A. :   *The Bombay Dockyard and the Wadia Master Builders* (Ruttonjee Wadia, Bombay, 1955).
CHARNOCK, JOHN :   *An History of Marine Architecture* (London, 1802).
BROWNING, ANDREW (ED.) :   *English Historical Documents, 1660–1714* (Eyre and Spottiswoode, 1953).
WILSON, E. M. CARUS :   *Medieval Merchant Venturers* (Methuen, 1954).
WILLIAMSON, J. A. :   *Hawkins of Plymouth* (A. and C. Black, 1949).
QUENNELL, MARJORIE, and C. H. B. :   *A History of Everyday Things in England, 1500–1799* (fifth edition, Batsford, 1950).

INDEX